Essential Mathematics
for GCSE Foundation tier

Homework book

Michael White

Elmwood Press

First published 2006 by
Elmwood Press
80 Attimore Road
Welwyn Garden City
Herts AL8 6LP
Tel. 01707 333232

ISBN 978 1 902 214 658

© Michael White

Typeset and illustrated by TnQ Books and Journals Pvt. Ltd., Chennai, India.
Printed by WS Bookwell, Finland.

Contents

NUMBER 1   **1**

TASK 1.1

M

1 What is the value of the underlined digit in each number below:
   a 3<u>2</u>6   **b** <u>5</u>18   **c** 6<u>1</u>73   **d** <u>4</u>953   **e** 20<u>4</u>

2 $\boxed{5}$ $\boxed{3}$ $\boxed{4}$

   a Using all the 3 cards above, what is the *smallest* number you can make?
   b Using all the 3 cards above, what is the *largest* number you can make?

3 Jamie bought a new sofa for £1350. Write down the value of the 5 digit.

4 Annie sold her car for £5750. Write down the value of the 7 digit.

E

1 The 7 in the number 24·73 means $\frac{7}{10}$. What is the value of the underlined digit in each number below:
   a 0·6<u>9</u>   **b** 0·4<u>3</u>7   **c** 0·32<u>8</u>   **d** 0·<u>5</u>8
   e 9·71<u>4</u>   **f** 3·<u>6</u>28   **g** <u>2</u>3·748   **h** 46·20<u>7</u>

2 Which number is the smaller: $\boxed{0·03}$ or $\boxed{0·3}$

3 Which number is the larger: $\boxed{0·6}$ or $\boxed{0·09}$

4 Which number is the smallest: $\boxed{0·7}$ $\boxed{0·008}$ $\boxed{0·06}$

TASK 1.2

M

1 Round to the nearest 10.
   a 38   **b** 43   **c** 84   **d** 75   **e** 328

2 Round to the nearest 100.
   a 340   **b** 764   **c** 350   **d** 1240   **e** 1550

3 Round to the nearest 1000.

    a 3700   **b** 5550   **c** 7143   **d** 4238   **e** 6500

4 Carl has £13·64. Round this to the nearest pound.

5 Maria weighs 54·37 kg. Round this to the nearest kilogram.

6 Round to the nearest whole number.

    a 6·8   **b** 4·5   **c** 7·6   **d** 13·2   **e** 18·5

E

1 Work out these answers *with a calculator* and then round off the answers to the *nearest whole number.*

    a $7 \cdot 1 \times 3 \cdot 89$ **b** $6 \cdot 31 \times 4 \cdot 75$ **c** $5 \cdot 08 \times 3 \cdot 17$ **d** $693 \div 19$

    e $512 \div 4 \cdot 67$ **f** $71 \cdot 4 \div 5 \cdot 26$ **g** $5 \cdot 61 \div 13$ **h** $6 \cdot 82 \times 1 \cdot 78$

2 One evening around 300 people visit a nightclub. This number is rounded off to the nearest 100. Which of the numbers below could be the exact number of people at the nightclub?

    260   349   249   359   302   393   287   238

3 Round off 16 456 to

    a the nearest 10   **b** the nearest 100   **c** the nearest 1000.

TASK 1.3

M

Copy and complete.

1
```
  47
+ 64
────
```

2
```
  564
+ 239
─────
```

3
```
  3127
+ 4386
──────
```

4
```
  64
- 37
────
```

5
```
  83
- 48
────
```

6
```
  481
- 264
─────
```

7
```
  598
- 319
─────
```

8
```
  4628
- 1386
──────
```

9
```
  6217
- 4406
──────
```

10
```
  38742
+ 12638
───────
```

11 $387 + 519$ **12** $462 - 181$ **13** $1374 - 648$

E

1 Hannah has saved £415. She wants to buy a music centre costing £694. How much more money must she save?

2 The following people collect money for a Cancer charity.

| Ellie £138 | Dan £193 | Shalina £68 |

| Katie £89 | Callum £47 | Jack £204 |

How much money have they collected in total?

3 Find the difference between 592 and 176.

4 Marcus is taking part in a 1290 mile car rally. He has completed 863 miles. How many more miles must he cover?

Copy and complete Questions **5** to **10** by writing the missing number in the box.

5 $360 + \boxed{} = 589$ **6** $270 + \boxed{} = 440$ **7** $348 - \boxed{} = 230$

8 $712 - \boxed{} = 508$ **9** $1365 - \boxed{} = 980$ **10** $\boxed{} - 286 = 461$

TASK 1.4

M

1 Work out
 a 72×100 **b** 4160×10 **c** $586\,000 \div 10$
 d $673\,000 \div 100$ **e** 570×100 **f** 6720×1000

2 Copy and complete
 a $\boxed{} \div 100 = 47$ **b** $\boxed{} \times 100 = 3800$ **c** $\boxed{} \times 10 = 4800$
 d $160 \times \boxed{} = 16\,000$ **e** $36\,000 \div \boxed{} = 3600$ **f** $\boxed{} \times 100 = 72\,000$
 g $\boxed{} \to \boxed{\times 100} \to \boxed{21\,500} \to \boxed{\div 10} \to \boxed{} \to \boxed{\times 100} \to \boxed{}$

3 A group of 100 people won £8 000 000 on the National Lottery. How much money did each person win if they each received an equal share?

E

1 Work out
 a 20×60 **b** 900×30 **c** $1500 \div 30$
 d $6400 \div 800$ **e** $36\,000 \div 90$ **f** 400×700

2 Copy and complete
 a $\boxed{} \times 40 = 3200$ **b** $\boxed{} \times 200 = 8000$ **c** $\boxed{} \times 90 = 540$
 d $\boxed{} \div 50 = 60$ **e** $72\,000 \div \boxed{} = 90$ **f** $\boxed{} \div 300 = 70$

3 30 houses each costing £90 000 are built on a housing estate. What is the *total* cost of all 30 houses?

TASK 1.5

M

Work out

1
$$42 \times 4$$

2
$$63 \times 5$$

3
$$37 \times 8$$

4 49×3

5 6×84

6
$$304 \times 3$$

7
$$526 \times 4$$

8
$$463 \times 8$$

9 738×6

10 9×284

11 629 students at a school each pay £6 to go on a school trip. How much money do they pay *in total*?

E

Work out without a calculator.

1 32×14
2 17×24
3 42×23
4 64×34
5 213×15
6 421×36
7 839×28
8 627×56

9 One evening a restaurant sells 37 set dinners at £16 each. How much money does the restaurant receive *in total* for these 37 meals?

10 At the World Cup there were 24 teams. If each team had a squad of 26 players, how many players were there *in total*?

TASK 1.6

M

Work out

1 $48 \div 6$
2 $28 \div 4$
3 $36 \div 9$
4 $72 \div 8$
5 $56 \div 7$
6 $3\overline{)69}$
7 $4\overline{)136}$
8 $6\overline{)438}$
9 $8\overline{)296}$
10 $7\overline{)1512}$
11 $384 \div 8$
12 $354 \div 6$
13 $375 \div 5$
14 $2457 \div 7$
15 $2898 \div 6$

E

Work out each answer, giving the remainder.

1 $4\overline{)583}$
2 $5\overline{)712}$
3 $8\overline{)316}$
4 $6\overline{)2715}$
5 $9\overline{)4814}$
6 $828 \div 7$
7 $486 \div 5$
8 $377 \div 8$
9 $4386 \div 7$
10 $7245 \div 4$

11 43 children are playing in a 5-a-side tournament. How many complete teams of 5 players can be made?

12 A calculator costs £7. How many calculators can a school buy for £225?

13 A wine box at a supermarket can hold 6 bottles. How many boxes
    are needed to hold 112 bottles?

TASK 1.7

M

Work out

1 448 ÷ 16   2 612 ÷ 17   3 575 ÷ 23   4 576 ÷ 36
5 986 ÷ 29   6 774 ÷ 18   7 988 ÷ 26   8 722 ÷ 38

E

1 A book of stamps contains 36 stamps. How many books must I buy if
   I need 850 stamps?

2 1500 sweets are shared equally into 46 packets. How many
   sweets will be in each packet and how many sweets will be
   left over?

3 Which answer is the odd one out?

   | 891 ÷ 33 | | 406 ÷ 14 | | 648 ÷ 24 |
        A   B   C

4 One coach may carry 47 people. How many coaches are needed to
   transport 560 football fans to an away match?

5 37 screws are used to make a flat pack desk. If a factory has
   623 screws remaining, how may flat packs could the factory supply?

TASK 1.8

M

1
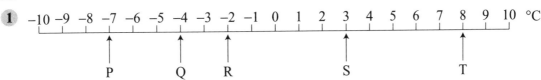

The *difference* in temperature between Q and R is 2 °C. Give the
difference in temperature between:
  a R and S   b Q and S   c R and T   d P and T

2 The temperature in Liverpool is $-3\,°C$ and the temperature in Plymouth is $2\,°C$. How much *warmer* is Plymouth than Liverpool?

3 The temperature in Hull is $-1\,°C$. The temperature rises by $8\,°C$. What is the new temperature in Hull?

4 Work out
a $2 - 7$ **b** $-3 - 2$ **c** $-4 + 1$ **d** $-9 - 2$ **e** $-6 + 5$

5 What is the *difference* between the two smallest numbers below?

4	-6	-3	1	5	-4

E

1 Work out
a $5 - -3$ **b** $7 + -4$ **c** $-2 - 3$ **d** $-5 - 1$ **e** $-6 + 2$
f $-7 - -1$ **g** $-4 - -4$ **h** $-3 + -6$ **i** $-2 + -6$ **j** $-6 - -6$

2 Copy and complete the boxes below:
a $3 - \boxed{} = -5$ **b** $\boxed{} - 1 = -4$ **c** $-9 + \boxed{} = -3$
d $\boxed{} - -4 = -2$ **e** $-4 - \boxed{} = -10$ **f** $\boxed{} + -7 = -5$

3 Work out
a $-4 + 2 - 3$ **b** $-1 - 6 + 4$ **c** $-9 + 6 - -1$
d $-2 + -3 + -4$ **e** $-8 - -6 + -3$ **f** $-3 - 9 - -4 - 2$

TASK 1.9

M

1 Work out
a 6×-4 **b** -3×8
c -2×-4 **d** $-10 \div 2$
e $-28 \div -4$ **f** $-30 \div -5$
g -7×-6 **h** -9×8
i $48 \div -6$ **j** -6×9
k $-35 \div 7$ **l** $-30 \div 6$
m $-81 \div -9$ **n** -7×-8

2 Copy and complete the multiplication square below:

$\times$	-4		-8	
3	-12			
			40	-45
	-24	-12		
		24		

E

Each empty square contains either a number or an operation ($+$, $-$, $\times$, $\div$).
Copy each square and fill in the missing details. The arrows are equals signs.

1

16	÷		→	−4
÷	▨	×	▨	▨
−8	+	5	→	
↓	▨	↓	▨	▨
	×		→	

2

−3	×		→	12
	▨	×	▨	
−7	−	−6	→	
↓	▨	↓	▨	
21	−		→	

3

−15	+	−5	→	
÷	▨	×	▨	
			→	−3
↓	▨	↓	▨	
3		−10	→	13

TASK 1.10

M

1 Work out
   a $6 + 4 \times 2$ **b** $5 + 2 \times 3$ **c** $(3 + 2) \times 6$ **d** $32 \div 4 + 6$
   e $4 \times 7 + 3$ **f** $30 \div (4 + 1)$ **g** $6 \times (9 - 3)$ **h** $5 + 6 \times 3 + 2$
   i $(5 + 4) \div 3 + 7$ **j** $(5 + 7) \div (6 - 2)$ **k** $28 - 3 \times 6$ **l** $4 + 6 \times 2 \div 2$
   m $(8 - 3) \times (4 + 5)$ **n** $(8 + 3 + 9) \div 5$ **o** $36 \div (2 + 7)$ **p** $(4 + 16) \div (8 - 3)$

E

1 Work out
   a $28 + 12 \times 3$ **b** $(28 + 12) \times 3$ **c** $63 - 14 \times 3$ **d** $21 + 20 \div 2$
   e $56 \div (3 + 5)$ **f** $(13 + 17) \times (62 - 12)$ **g** $4 + 16 \times 5$ **h** $50 - 100 \div 4$
   i $72 \div 8 - 32 \div 4$ **j** $28 + 48 \div 12$ **k** $31 - 9 \times 3 + 16$ **l** $39 + 63 \div 7$

2 Copy each Question and write brackets so that each calculation gives
   the correct answer.
   a $7 \times 4 + 2 = 42$ **b** $6 + 9 \div 3 = 5$ **c** $6 + 3 \times 4 = 36$ **d** $4 + 3 \times 8 - 6 = 14$
   e $12 + 6 \div 9 = 2$ **f** $15 - 6 \times 3 + 6 = 81$ **g** $8 \times 4 - 2 = 16$ **h** $72 \div 2 + 6 = 9$

NUMBER 2   **2**

TASK 2.1

M

1 $3^2 = 3 \times 3 = 9$. Find the value of
   a 5^2 **b** 7^2 **c** 6^2 **d** 1^2 **e** 30^2

2 $\sqrt{49} = 7$ because $7 \times 7 = 49$. Find the value of

    a $\sqrt{16}$ **b** $\sqrt{36}$ **c** $\sqrt{100}$ **d** $\sqrt{64}$ **e** $\sqrt{1}$

3 What is the length of one side of this square?

area = 25 cm²

4 Write down the square root of 400.

5 Find the value of

    a $3^2 + 4^2$ **b** $9^2 - 4^2$ **c** $(8 - 2)^2$

    d $10^2 + 6^2$ **e** $\sqrt{81} - \sqrt{4}$ **f** $\sqrt{16} + \sqrt{25}$

    g $\sqrt{(28 + 21)}$ **h** $\sqrt{(63 - 59)}$ **i** $\sqrt{(6^2 + 8^2)}$

E

1 $7^3 = 7 \times 7 \times 7 = 49 \times 7 = 343$. Find the value of

    a 2^3 **b** 4^3 **c** 1^3 **d** 5^3 **e** 10^3

2 How many small cubes are needed to make this giant cube?

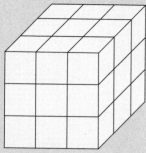

3 $\sqrt[3]{64} = 4$ because $4 \times 4 \times 4 = 64$. Find the value of

    a $\sqrt[3]{8}$ **b** $\sqrt[3]{1}$ **c** $\sqrt[3]{125}$ **d** $\sqrt[3]{27}$

4 Write down the cube root of 1000.

5 Find the value of

    a $\sqrt[3]{(5 + 3)}$ **b** $\sqrt[3]{(6^2 + 4^2 + 12)}$ **c** $(3^2 - 2^2)^3$

TASK 2.2

M only

1 $4 \times 4 \times 4 \times 4 \times 4$ means '4 to the power 5' which is written as 4^5 (*index form*). Write the following in index form.

    a $3 \times 3 \times 3 \times 3$ **b** $2 \times 2 \times 2 \times 2 \times 2 \times 2$

    c $7 \times 7 \times 7 \times 7 \times 7$ **d** $10 \times 10 \times 10$

2 3^5 means $3 \times 3 \times 3 \times 3 \times 3$. Copy and complete the following:

    a 9^4 means ....   **b** 5^4 means ....

    c 6^6 means ....   **d** 2^7 means ....

3 Which is smaller? $\boxed{3^2}$ or $\boxed{2^3}$

4 Which is smaller? $\boxed{5^2}$ or $\boxed{2^5}$

5 Find the value of

    a 2×3^2 **b** $3^3 \times 4$ **c** $5^3 \times 2^2$

Use a calculator for the Questions below:

6 Find the value of

    a 5^4 **b** 3^6 **c** $4 \times 4 \times 4 \times 4 \times 4$ **d** 10^5

    e 7^5 **f** 2^{12} **g** 6 to the power 7   **h** $3 \times 3 \times 3 \times 3 \times 3$

    i $8 \times 8 \times 8 \times 8$ **j** 3^8 **k** 4^7 **l** 8 to the power 6

7 Write down the next two numbers in this sequence:

    3, 9, 27, 81, 243, ..., ...

8 How many numbers are in the sequence below up to and including 512?

    2, 4, 8, 16, ..., 512

TASK 2.3

M

Write down *all* the factors of the following numbers:

1 20 (6 factors)   **2** 12 (6 factors)   **3** 29 (2 factors)

4 18   **5** 32   **6** 50

7 Which of these numbers are:

    a even numbers?   **b** odd numbers?

    c prime numbers?   **d** factors of 24?

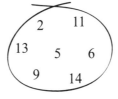

8 Write down *all* the *even* factors of 24.

9 Write down *all* the factors of 35 which are *prime*.

10 Which numbers between 30 and 40 have 4 as a factor?

E

1 Write down the first 5 multiples of:

    a 3   **b** 6   **c** 9   **d** 8   **e** 12

2 Which of these numbers are:
  a multiples of 6
  b multiples of 7
  c *not* multiples of 2

18 54
21 63
42 26
28

3 Copy and complete the first five multiples of 6 and 10.

<u>6</u>:   6   12   ☐   ☐   ☐
<u>10</u>:   10   ☐   ☐   ☐   ☐

Write down the <u>L</u>owest <u>C</u>ommon <u>M</u>ultiple of 6 and 10.

4 Find the Lowest Common Multiple of each of these pairs of numbers.
  a 5 and 8   **b** 8 and 12   **c** 10 and 60

5 Amy and Josh are racing each other. Amy takes 5 minutes to complete one lap. Josh takes 7 minutes to complete one lap. After how many minutes will Amy and Josh pass the starting point at exactly the same time?

TASK 2.4

M

1 **a** List all the factors of 18.
  b List all the factors of 30.
  c Write down the <u>H</u>ighest <u>C</u>ommon <u>F</u>actor of 18 and 30.

2 **a** List all the factors of 30.
  b List all the factors of 45.
  c Write down the Highest Common Factor of 30 and 45.

3 Find the Highest Common Factor of:
  a 20 and 50   **b** 25 and 60
  c 36 and 60   **d** 16, 32 and 40

E

1 Work out
  a $3 \times 3 \times 5$ **b** $2^2 \times 7$ **c** $2^2 \times 3^2$

2 For each Question below, find the number which belongs in the empty box:
  a $60 = 2^2 \times 3 \times \boxed{}$ **b** $40 = 2^3 \times \boxed{}$ **c** $126 = 2 \times 3^2 \times \boxed{}$

3 Using any method, write the following numbers as products of prime factors:

    a 75   **b** 44   **c** 80   **d** 594

4 $\boxed{1617 = 3 \times 7 \times 7 \times 11}$ and $\boxed{273 = 3 \times 7 \times 13}$

Find the Highest Common Factor of 273 and 1617.

5 Write 315 and 495 as products of prime factors. Use this to find the Highest Common Factor of 315 and 495.

6 Write 396 and 420 as products of prime factors. Use this to find the Highest Common Factor of 396 and 420.

TASK 2.5

M

1 Which shapes have an equivalent fraction shaded?

    A   B   C

2 Copy this rectangle.
Shade a fraction equivalent to $\frac{3}{5}$.

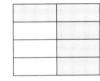

3 Copy and complete these equivalent fractions by filling in the box.

    a $\frac{3}{4} = \frac{\square}{20}$ **b** $\frac{1}{3} = \frac{\square}{12}$ **c** $\frac{5}{8} = \frac{10}{\square}$ **d** $\frac{2}{9} = \frac{\square}{36}$

    e $\frac{3}{8} = \frac{15}{\square}$ **f** $\frac{7}{20} = \frac{35}{\square}$ **g** $\frac{4}{5} = \frac{\square}{30}$ **h** $\frac{5}{9} = \frac{45}{\square}$

E

1 Cancel each fraction below to its lowest terms.

    a $\frac{18}{20}$ **b** $\frac{12}{30}$ **c** $\frac{6}{15}$ **d** $\frac{24}{32}$ **e** $\frac{6}{18}$

    f $\frac{25}{100}$ **g** $\frac{21}{28}$ **h** $\frac{32}{48}$ **i** $\frac{63}{81}$ **j** $\frac{88}{121}$

2 Which of the fractions below are the same as $\frac{7}{8}$?

a $\frac{21}{24}$ b $\frac{16}{18}$ c $\frac{14}{24}$ d $\frac{35}{40}$ e $\frac{21}{27}$ f $\frac{56}{64}$

3 Find the fractions in the table which are equivalent to $\frac{4}{9}$.
Rearrange the chosen letters to show a salad vegetable.

$\frac{32}{72}$	$\frac{40}{90}$	$\frac{12}{20}$	$\frac{45}{81}$	$\frac{28}{63}$	$\frac{20}{45}$	$\frac{28}{56}$	$\frac{12}{27}$	$\frac{16}{45}$	$\frac{24}{54}$
D	H	B	U	S	A	M	R	Y	I

TASK 2.6

M only

1 Copy and use the diagrams to *explain* why $\frac{2}{3}$ is larger than $\frac{7}{12}$.

2·6 dw Tues 10th

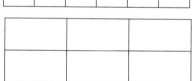

2 a $\frac{1}{2} = \frac{\square}{16}$ b Which is larger, $\frac{1}{2}$ or $\frac{9}{16}$?

3 Write down the *smaller* fraction:

a $\frac{5}{8}$ or $\frac{3}{4}$ b $\frac{9}{10}$ or $\frac{26}{30}$ c $\frac{6}{7}$ or $\frac{7}{8}$

4 Place in order, *largest first*:

a $\frac{7}{20}, \frac{1}{4}, \frac{3}{10}$ b $\frac{11}{16}, \frac{5}{8}, \frac{19}{32}$

c $\frac{13}{18}, \frac{2}{3}, \frac{5}{9}$ d $\frac{1}{8}, \frac{5}{48}, \frac{1}{6}$

5 a $\frac{3}{8} = \frac{\square}{16}$ b $\frac{1}{2} = \frac{\square}{16}$ c Does $\frac{7}{16}$ lie between $\frac{3}{8}$ and $\frac{1}{2}$?

6 a $\frac{1}{4} = \frac{\square}{40}$ b $\frac{3}{10} = \frac{\square}{40}$ c Write down a fraction which lies between $\frac{1}{4}$ and $\frac{3}{10}$.

7 **a** $\frac{5}{7} = \frac{\square}{35}$ **b** $\frac{4}{5} = \frac{\square}{35}$ **c** Write down a fraction which lies between $\frac{5}{7}$ and $\frac{4}{5}$.

8 For each pair of fractions below, write down a fraction which lies between them:

a $\frac{4}{15}$ and $\frac{1}{3}$ **b** $\frac{5}{6}$ and $\frac{11}{12}$ **c** $\frac{7}{10}$ and $\frac{8}{10}$

TASK 2.7

M

1 Is 0.027 the same as $\frac{27}{1000}$?

2 Is 0.8 the same as $\frac{4}{5}$?

3 Is 0.45 the same as $\frac{7}{20}$?

4 Change the following decimals to fractions in their most simple form.

a 0.03 **b** 0.82 **c** 0.4 **d** 0.052 **e** 0.15

5 Copy the Questions below and fill in the boxes.

a $\frac{11}{20} = \frac{\square}{100} = 0.\square$ **b** $\frac{7}{200} = \frac{\square}{1000} = 0.\square$

6 Convert the fractions below to decimals.

a $\frac{3}{20}$ **b** $\frac{19}{25}$ **c** $\frac{103}{200}$ **d** $\frac{3}{8}$ **e** $\frac{13}{25}$

7 Change the fractions below to decimals by dividing the numerator by the denominator.

a $\frac{5}{9}$ **b** $\frac{1}{11}$ **c** $\frac{5}{12}$

E

1 Which is larger?

a 0.06 or 0.5 **b** 0.038 or 0.04 **c** 0.74 or 0.742

2 $0.03 > 0.026$ Is this true or false?

3 $0.6 < 0.546$ Is this true or false?

4 For each set of numbers below, arrange the numbers in order of size, smallest first.
  a 0·03, 0·3, 0·003
  b 0·91, 0·902, 0·92, 0·091
  c 0·073, 0·07, 0·75, 0·712
  d 0·418, 0·408, 0·48, 0·048
  e 7·06, 7·1, 7·102, 7·07, 7·13

5 In the Questions below, answer True or False.
  a 0·08 is more than 0·7   **b** 0·603 is more than 0·068
  c 0·36 is more than 0·308   **d** 0·4 is less than 0·38
  e 0·027 is less than 0·03   **f** 0·056 is more than 0·07

SHAPE 1   3

TASK 3.1

M

1 For each of these angles say whether they are acute, obtuse or reflex:

2 Copy and complete the sentences below:
  a An acute angle is less than _____.
  b An obtuse angle is more than _____ and less than _____.
  c A reflex angle is more than _____.

3 Which of the angles below are obtuse?
  187°   45°   120°   193°   243°   138°   31°

4 Draw a triangle where all the angles are acute.

5 Can you draw a triangle which has two obtuse angles inside it?

6 How many obtuse angles can you
see in this trapezium?

E

1 The angle BCD is obtuse.
Is angle ADC acute or obtuse?

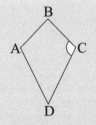

2 **a** Is ∠QRS acute or obtuse?
  b Is ∠SPQ acute or obtuse?

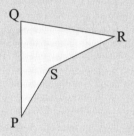

3 Name the marked angles below:

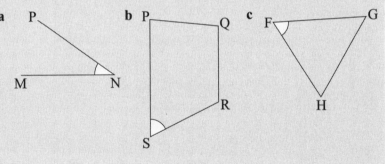

4 *Estimate* the size of each angle stated below:

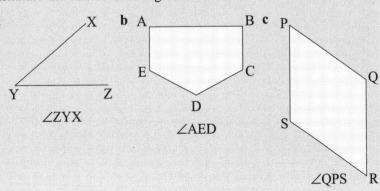

TASK 3.2

M

Find the angles marked with the letters.

1

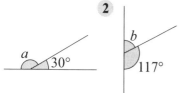

a 30°

2

b 117°

3

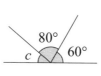

80° 60°
c

4

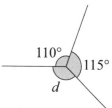

110° 115°
d

5

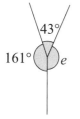

43°
161° e

6

79° f 64°

7

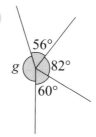

56°
g 82°
60°

8

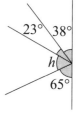

23° 38°
h
65°

E

1 **a** Draw 2 perpendicular lines.
   b How large is the angle between the 2 perpendicular lines?

2 Draw a triangle which has 2 sides which are perpendicular to each other.

In the Questions below, find the angles marked with the letters.

3

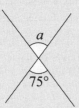

a
75°

4

38°
b 76°

5

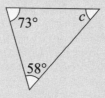

73° c
58°

6

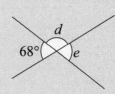

d
68° e

7

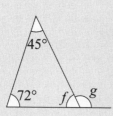

45°
72° f g

8

53°
h
82° i

9

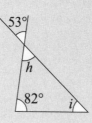

k
j
146°

10

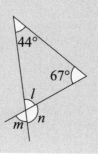

44°
67°
l
m n

TASK 3.3

M

Find the angles marked with the letters.

1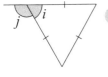

2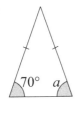

3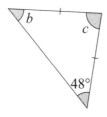

4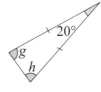

5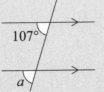

6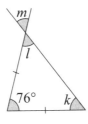

7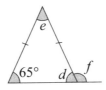

8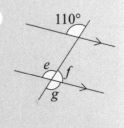

E

Find the angles marked with the letters.

1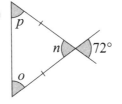

2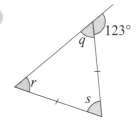

3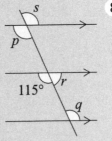

4

5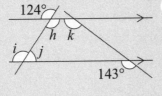

6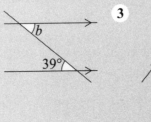

7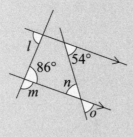

8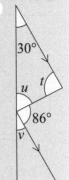

TASK 3.4

M

1 Each of these shapes have a line of symmetry.
Copy them into your book and draw on a dotted line to show the *line of symmetry*:

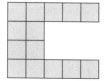 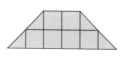

2 Copy the patterns below on squared paper. Shade in as many squares as necessary to complete the symmetrical patterns. The dotted lines are lines of symmetry.

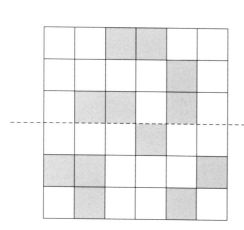 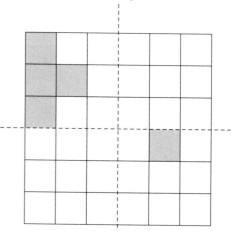

3 Sketch these shapes in your book and draw on *all* the *lines of symmetry*.

  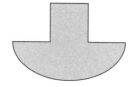

E

For each shape write the *order* of *rotational symmetry* (you may use tracing paper).

1    **2**   **3** 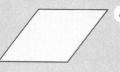   **4**

5

6

7

8

9 Draw your own shape which has an order of rotational symmetry of 3.

10 Draw a triangle which has *no* rotational symmetry.

TASK 3.5

M only

1 How many planes of symmetry does this triangular prism have?

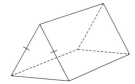

2 Draw each shape below and show one plane of symmetry.

a

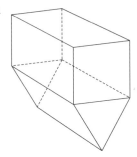

b

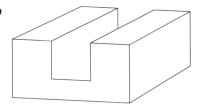

c

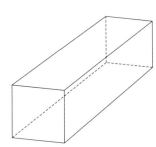

d

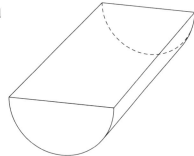

3 How many planes of symmetry does a cube have?

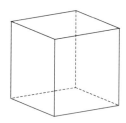

TASK 3.6

M

1 Draw a parallelogram.

2 How many lines of symmetry does a parallelogram have?

3 Draw a quadrilateral which has two lines of symmetry *only*.

4 Name this shape:

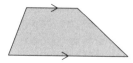

5 Draw a rhombus in your book.
Draw in the two *diagonals*.
At the point of intersection of the two diagonals,
write down the angle between the diagonals.

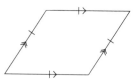

6 Draw a quadrilateral which has no lines of symmetry.

7 Copy and complete the two sentences below:
A parallelogram has two pairs of e _ _ _ _ opposite sides and two
pairs of p _ _ _ _ _ _ _ opposite sides. The diagonals cut each
other in h _ _ _.

8 What is the *order* of rotational symmetry of a kite?

E

Find the angles marked with letters.

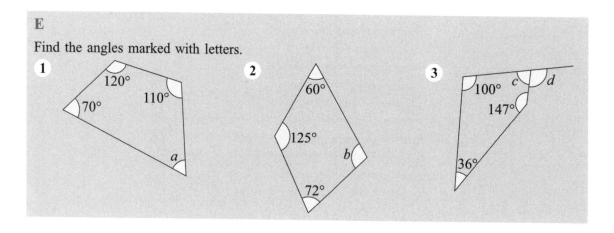

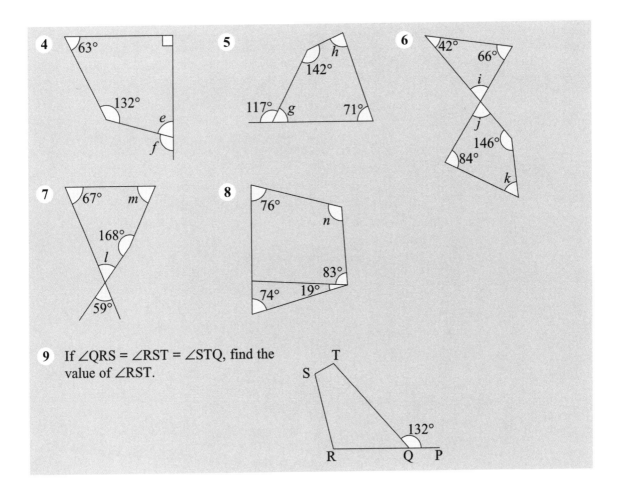

9 If ∠QRS = ∠RST = ∠STQ, find the value of ∠RST.

TASK 3.7

M

Find the angles marked with letters.

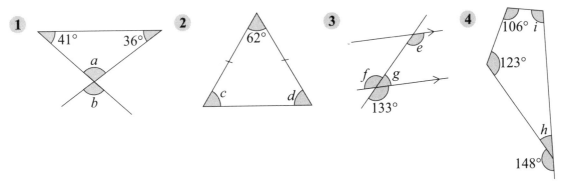

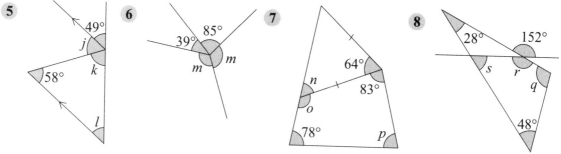

5 49° j k 58° l

6 39° 85° m m

7 64° n 83° o 78° p

8 28° 152° s r q 48°

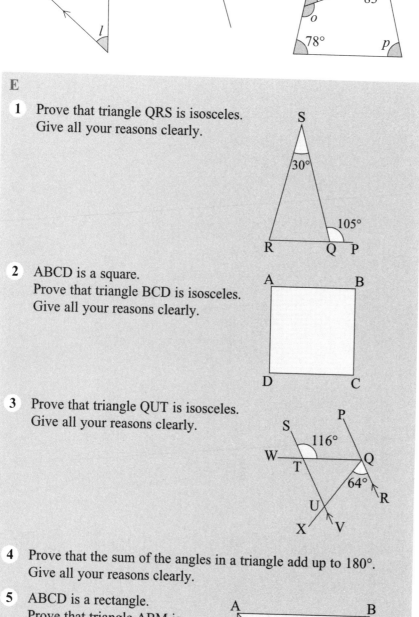

E

1 Prove that triangle QRS is isosceles.
Give all your reasons clearly.

S 30° 105° R Q P

2 ABCD is a square.
Prove that triangle BCD is isosceles.
Give all your reasons clearly.

A B D C

3 Prove that triangle QUT is isosceles.
Give all your reasons clearly.

S P 116° W T Q 64° R U X V

4 Prove that the sum of the angles in a triangle add up to 180°.
Give all your reasons clearly.

5 ABCD is a rectangle.
Prove that triangle ABM is isosceles.
Give all your reasons clearly.

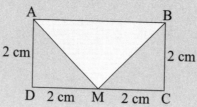

A B 2 cm 2 cm D 2 cm M 2 cm C

TASK 3.8

M only

1 Copy and complete the sentence:
'The exterior angles of a polygon add up to _____.'

2 An octagon has 8 sides. Find the size of each exterior angle of a *regular* octagon.

3 A decagon has 10 sides.
  a Find the size of each exterior angle of a *regular* decagon.
  b Find the size of each interior angle of a *regular* decagon.

4 Find the size of angle *a*.

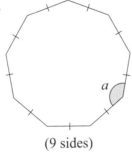

(9 sides)

5 Find the exterior angles of *regular* polygons with
  a 18 sides   b 24 sides   c 45 sides

6 Find the interior angle of each polygon in Question 5.

7 The exterior angle of a *regular* polygon is 24°. How many sides has the polygon?

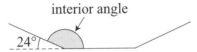

interior angle

24°

8 The interior angle of a *regular* polygon is 162°. How many sides has the polygon?

ALGEBRA 1   4

TASK 4.1

M

In Questions 1 to 20 find the value of each expression when $p = 4$
$q = 3$
$r = 7$

1 $3p$ **2** qr **3** $5p + 7$ **4** $2p + 5r$

5 $8q - 2r$ **6** p^2 **7** $r - 2q$ **8** r^2

9 $q^2 + r^2$ **10** $8(p - q)$ **11** $9(2r - p)$ **12** $q(6p + 2q)$

13 $r(3r - 4q)$ **14** $\dfrac{8q}{p}$ **15** $9q + 6$ **16** $\dfrac{2p + 2q}{r}$

17 $\dfrac{6(p + q)}{r}$ **18** $p^2 + q^2 + r^2$ **19** pqr **20** $5p + 6q - 3r$

In Questions **21** to **23** find the value of each expression:

21 $20 - 2y$ if $y = 5$ **22** $9(3a + 1)$ if $a = 2$ **23** $8m + m^2$ if $m = 4$

E

In Questions **1** to **20** find the value of each expression when $f = -1$
$$g = 5$$
$$h = -4$$

1 $2h$ **2** $3f$ **3** fg **4** fh

5 $2g - h$ **6** $3f + 4g$ **7** $4f + 3g$ **8** h^2

9 $g^2 + h^2$ **10** $16 - h$ **11** $f + g + h$ **12** $5g + 6f$

13 $6h + 10$ **14** $3(f + g)$ **15** $7(g - f)$ **16** $(4f)^2$

17 $4g - 3f + 3h$ **18** $\dfrac{6h}{2f}$ **19** $\dfrac{7(f + g)}{h}$ **20** $2h^2$

In Questions **21** to **23** find the value of each expression:

21 $3b + 6$ if $b = -2$ **22** $4(2 - 3x)$ if $x = -6$ **23** $9(n^2 - 20)$ if $n = -5$

TASK 4.2

M

1 $c = 4d - 3$
Find c when $d = 5$.

2 $y = 5x + 6$
Find y when $x = 7$.

3 $m = \dfrac{p}{4} - 8$
Find m when $p = 40$.

4 $A = 6(B + 2)$
Find A when $B = 7$.

5 $V = IR$
Find V when $I = 7$ and $R = 15$.

6 $f = \dfrac{2u}{v}$
Find f when $u = 16$ and $v = 4$.

7 $y = 5(2x + 6y)$
Find y when $x = 4$ and $y = 7$.

8 $P = \dfrac{Q}{6} + 4R$
Find P when $Q = 48$ and $R = 13$.

9 $A = r^2 + wr$

Use a calculator to find the value of A when $r = 3\cdot6$ and $w = 1\cdot4$.

10 $V = lwh + 4wh$

Use a calculator to find the value of V when $l = 8\cdot4$, $w = 0\cdot9$ and $h = 3\cdot8$.

E

1 Below are several different formulas for p in terms of n. Find the value of p in each case.
  a $p = 8n + 7$ when $n = 0\cdot5$
  b $p = 6(4n - 1)$ when $n = 5$
  c $p = \frac{3n}{2} + n^2$ when $n = 6$

2 The total surface area A of this cuboid is given by the formula
$A = 2lw + 2lh + 2hw$
Find the value of A when
  a $l = 5$, $w = 3$ and $h = 1$
  b $l = 10$, $w = 2\cdot5$ and $h = 4$

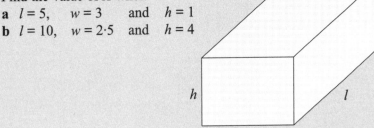

3 Find the value of y using formulas and values given below:
  a $y = 4x + c$ when $x = 17$ and $c = -3$
  b $y = x^2 - b$ when $x = -3$ and $b = 2$
  c $y = \frac{x}{9} + \frac{z}{4}$ when $x = 54$ and $z = 68$
  d $y = x^2 + 8x$ when $x = -10$

4 The surface area A of a sphere is given by the formula $A = 12r^2$
Find the value of A when
  a $r = 3$ **b** $r = 5$ **c** $r = 8$

5 Energy E is given by the formula $E = mc^2$ where m is the mass and c is the speed of light.
Find the value of E when $m = 15$ and $c = 300\,000\,000$.

6 Using the formula $M = 7P - Q$, find the value of M when
  a $P = -8$ and $Q = 19$ **b** $P = -15$ and $Q = -88$

TASK 4.3

M

Collect like terms

1 $9x + 4y + 5y$

2 $5p + 6q + 3p$

3 $8a + 2b + 4b + 5a$

4 $4m - 2m + 8p + p$

5 $4a + 6b - b$

6 $4f + 3f + 6g - 5f$

7 $3a + 6b + 3b - 4b$

8 $9p - 4p + q$

9 $4m + 6q - 3q - 2m$

10 $5a + 8b - 7b - 4a$

11 $2x - x + 6y - y$

12 $5m + 2p - 3m + 9q - p$

13 Copy and complete the pyramids below. The answer for each box is found by adding the 2 boxes *below* it.

a

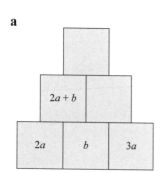

b

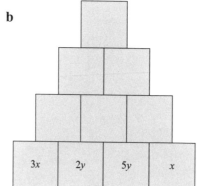

c

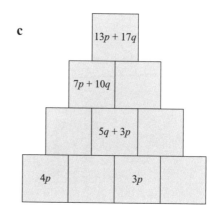

E

Simplify

1 $-5b + 2b$

2 $-4x + 9x$

3 $-7y + 5y$

4 $3p - 6p + 9q$

5 $4a + 7b - b - 6a$

6 $5x + 2 + 3x$

7 $5c + 2 - 8c + 1$

8 $6 + 3m - 5m$

9 $3f + 6f + 4$

10 $7a^2 + 3a^2 + 5a^2$

11 $8x^2 - 6x^2 + x^2$

12 $5ab + 10ab - 7ab$

13 $12xy + 3x - 6xy$

14 $9mn + 4 + 3mn$

15 $6p^2 - p$

16 $5m^2 - 3m + 4m^2$

17 $a + b + ab + 4a$

18 $4a^2 + 6ab - 4ab + 3a^2$

19 The expression in each bag shows how much money is in it. Find and simplify an expression for the money Jack spends if he uses all the money in:

a bags A and B

b bags A and C

c all 3 bags

A

B

C

20 Darryl is $(4a^2 + 6ab)$ years old. Christine is $(3a + 2ab)$ years old and Rory is $(ab - a^2)$ years old. Find and simplify an expression for their *total* ages.

TASK 4.4

M

Do the following multiplications and divisions:

1 $3a \times 3$ **2** $2b \times 4$ **3** $7m \times 3$ **4** $5 \times 7n$

5 $6 \times 8y$ **6** $16x \div 2$ **7** $27y \div 3$ **8** $60a \div 10$

9 $12b \div 4$ **10** $8m \times 5$ **11** $n \times n$ **12** $y \times y$

13 $6a \times a$ **14** $9f \times f$ **15** $q \times 7q$ **16** $3y \times 2y$

17 $5b \times 3b$ **18** $8m \times 4p$ **19** $5a \times 9b$ **20** $10a \times 10a$

E

In Questions **1** to **9** answer 'true' or 'false'.

1 $a + b = ab$ **2** $a + a = a^2$ **3** $5m + m = 6m$

4 $6n^2 - n^2 = 6$ **5** $4y \times y = 4y^2$ **6** $7a \times 2b = 14ab$

7 $16x \div 4 = 12x$ **8** $a \times 5 \times b = 5ab$ **9** $y \times y \times y = y^3$

Simplify

10 $4a \times -6b$ **11** $-3m \times -2p$ **12** $-6a \div -3$

13 $-15x \div 5$ **14** $-5a \times -2a$ **15** $-9f \times -4g$

16 $-3p \times 7q$ **17** $8a \times -4c$ **18** $-a \times 3a$

19 $-6y \times 11$ **20** $3b \times -6b$ **21** $-42a^2 \div -2$

TASK 4.5

M

Copy and complete:

1 $3(a + 4) = \boxed{} + 12$ **2** $a(a + b) = a^2 + \boxed{}$

Multiply out

3 $5(m + 2)$ **4** $4(x - 3)$ **5** $6(a - 8)$

6 $2(3y + 5)$ **7** $9(2m - 4)$ **8** $3(x + y)$

9 $6(2a - b)$ **10** $5(m + 3p)$ **11** $7(2x + 5)$

12 $4(3p - 4q)$ **13** $a(b + c)$ **14** $x(x - y)$

15 $m(m - 3p)$ **16** $c(2d + 1)$ **17** $2p(p + q)$

Write down and *simplify* an expression for the area of each shape below:

18 $2a + b$

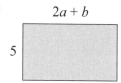

5

19 $4b - 1$

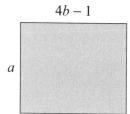

a

20 $m + 8p$

m

E

Copy and complete:

1 $-4(x + 7) = \boxed{} - 28$ **2** $-3(6b - 2) = -18b + \boxed{}$

Expand

3 $-3(a + 2)$ **4** $-6(b - 4)$ **5** $-5(x - 3)$

6 $-2(3m - 4)$ **7** $-a(b - c)$ **8** $-m(2 - p)$

9 $-y(x + z)$ **10** $-x(x + 3y)$ **11** $-(a - b)$

12 $-(p + q)$ **13** $-b(2a - 3)$ **14** $-f(5g + 2h)$

15 $-q(q - 8r)$ **16** $3a(3a + 4b)$ **17** $-8x(4x - 3y)$

TASK 4.6

M

Copy and complete:

1 $3(4a + 7) - 5a = \boxed{} + 21 - 5a = \boxed{} + 21$

2 $5(4x + 6) + 3(2x - 5) = \boxed{} + 30 + \boxed{} - 15 = \boxed{} + 15$

Simplify

3 $3(a + 4) + 7$ **4** $6(m + 4) - 9$

5 $5(x + 6) + 3x$ **6** $2(4y + 7) + 12$

7 $9(2b + 4) + 4b$ **8** $7(5a + 6) - 10a$

Expand and simplify

9 $3(x + 4) + 4(x + 2)$ **10** $2(4p + 3) + 5(p + 3)$

11 $6(2m + 5) + 3(4m + 1)$ **12** $7(3a + 2) + 4(a - 2)$

13 $3(8y + 6) + 2(2y - 5)$

14 $5n + 9 + 6(2x + 3)$

15 $4b + 9(3b + 6) - 24$

16 $7(4c + 7) + 3(2c - 8)$

E

Copy and complete:

1 $6(3a + 2) - 4(2a + 2) = \boxed{} + 12 - \boxed{} - 8 = \boxed{} + 4$

2 $7(4x + 3) - 5(3x - 6) = 28x + \boxed{} - 15x + \boxed{} = 13x + \boxed{}$

Simplify

3 $5(a + 4) - 3(a + 2)$

4 $6(2m + 3) - 5(m + 3)$

5 $8(2x + 5) - 4(x - 2)$

6 $4(6p + 4) - 3(3p - 5)$

7 $4(5y + 6) - 2(4y + 3)$

8 $2(8b + 9) - 4(4b - 6)$

9 $8a - 3(2a - 5) + 6$

10 $7x - 4(x - 1) - 3$

11 $9(4n + 7) - 5(2n + 4)$

12 $10q + 3(5 - 2q) + 4(7q + 4)$

TASK 4.7

M

1 Copy and complete the following:

a $(x + 2)\,(x + 5)$

$= x^2 + 5x + \boxed{} + 10$

$= x^2 + \boxed{} + 10$

b $(x + 7)\,(x + 3)$

$= x^2 + \boxed{} + 7x + \boxed{}$

$= x^2 + \boxed{} + \boxed{}$

c $(x + 8)\,(x + 2)$

$= \boxed{} + \boxed{} + 8x + 16$

$= \boxed{} + \boxed{} + 16$

Multiply out the following:

2 $(x + 4)\,(x + 6)$

3 $(m + 7)\,(m + 5)$

4 $(y + 10)\,(y + 4)$

5 $(n + 6)\,(n + 7)$

6 $(a + 2)\,(a + 9)$

7 $(x + 12)\,(x + 3)$

8 Work out the area of this square, giving your answer in terms of x.

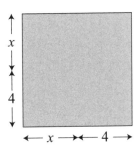

Expand:

9 $(x + 6)\,(x + 6)$

10 $(x + 7)^2$

11 $(x + 1)^2$

E

1 Copy and complete the following:

a $(x + 3)(x - 5)$

$$= x^2 - \boxed{} + 3x - 15$$
$$= x^2 - \boxed{} - 15$$

b $(y - 4)(y - 4)$

$$= y^2 - \boxed{} - 4y + \boxed{}$$
$$= y^2 - \boxed{} + \boxed{}$$

c $(n - 8)(n + 5)$

$$= \boxed{} + 5n - \boxed{} - 40$$
$$= \boxed{} - \boxed{} - 40$$

Expand:

2 $(x + 4)(x - 6)$

3 $(a - 6)(a - 5)$

4 $(y - 3)(y - 7)$

5 $(n - 9)(n + 4)$

6 $(m + 7)(m - 6)$

7 $(b + 5)(b - 8)$

8 $(a - 8)(a - 8)$

9 $(x - 3)(x - 4)$

10 $(f + 10)(f - 7)$

Multiply out the following:

11 $(n - 5)(n - 5)$

12 $(y - 7)^2$

13 $(a - 2)^2$

14 $(4 + x)(x + 7)$

15 $(p - 3)^2$

16 $(m + 2)(8 - m)$

TASK 4.8

M

Copy and complete

1 $4a + 6 = 2(2a + \boxed{})$

2 $6a + 2 = 2(3a + \boxed{})$

3 $6m - 9 = 3(2m - \boxed{})$

4 $18b - 12 = 6(\boxed{} - 2)$

5 $16y + 28 = 4(\boxed{} + \boxed{})$

6 $40x - 24 = 8(\boxed{} - \boxed{})$

Factorise the expressions below:

7 $6x + 10$

8 $8a + 12$

9 $10p - 40$

10 $20y - 25$

11 $12m + 9$

12 $36b - 12$

13 $9x + 6y$

14 $16a + 12b$

15 $24m - 20p$

16 $45f + 35g$

17 $21a - 15b$

18 $30x - 50y$

19 $8p + 6q - 10r$

20 $15x - 30y - 20z$

21 $35a - 21b + 49c$

E

Copy and complete

1 $ab + af = a(b + \boxed{})$

2 $xy - xz = x(\boxed{} - z)$

3 $4mp - 10m = 2m(2p - \boxed{})$

4 $n^2 + 7n = n(n + \boxed{})$

5 $f^2 - 9f = f(\boxed{} - 9)$

6 $4ab + 18bc = 2b(\boxed{} + \boxed{})$

Factorise the expressions below:

7 $xy + yz$

8 $a^2 - 6a$

9 $b^2 + 4b$

10 $c^2 + 9c$

11 $mp - pq$

12 $3xy + 9xz$

13 $10ab - 15ac$

14 $18wz - 15wy$

15 $12fg + 21f$

16 $4a^2 - 6a$	**17** $5p^2 - 30pq$	**18** $18mp + 30m$
19 $8pq - 20q^2$	**20** $16xyz - 28y^2$	**21** $33a^2 + 55abc$

NUMBER 3   5

TASK 5.1

M

1 Copy each shape below and shade in the given fraction.

a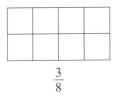

$\dfrac{3}{8}$

b

$\dfrac{3}{4}$

c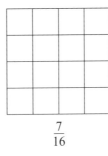

$\dfrac{7}{16}$

d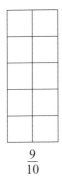

$\dfrac{9}{10}$

2 Find $\dfrac{1}{10}$ of: **a** 30   **b** 80   **c** 100   **d** 500

3 Find $\dfrac{1}{7}$ of: **a** 14   **b** 35   **c** 63   **d** 140

Work out:

4 $\dfrac{1}{5}$ of 35   **5** $\dfrac{2}{3}$ of 18   **6** $\dfrac{3}{8}$ of 56   **7** $\dfrac{5}{7}$ of 42

8 There are 30 students in a class. $\dfrac{2}{5}$ of them are girls. How many girls are there in the class?

9 In a spelling test full marks were 54. How many marks did Simon get if he got $\dfrac{5}{6}$ of full marks?

10 Maddy has 12 pairs of shoes. 4 pairs of shoes are black.
a What fraction of her shoes are black?
b What fraction of her shoes are *not* black?

11 In a food survey, 41 people were asked what their favourite meal was. 16 people chose 'pizza'.
a What fraction of the people chose 'pizza'?
b What fraction of the people did *not* choose 'pizza'?

12 What fraction of the months of the year begin with the letter J?

13 There are 60 minutes in 1 hour.
What fraction of 1 hour is:

    a 10 minutes   **b** 20 minutes
    c 45 minutes   **d** 50 minutes
    e 17 minutes   **f** 36 minutes
    (Try and cancel your answers)

E

Work out

1 $\frac{5}{7}$ of 63   **2** $\frac{5}{8}$ of 24   **3** $\frac{2}{9}$ of 72   **4** $\frac{3}{7}$ of 42

5 $\frac{5}{9}$ of 27   **6** $\frac{7}{8}$ of 64   **7** $\frac{1}{6}$ of 126   **8** $\frac{9}{50}$ of 400

9 A toaster costs £25. In a sale, the price of a toaster is reduced by $\frac{2}{5}$.
How much does a toaster cost now?

10 A packet of biscuits contains 276 g. If a packet of biscuits now has
$\frac{1}{3}$ extra, how much does it contain?

11 In seven years, a footballer scored 216 goals and $\frac{2}{9}$ of these were
headers. How many headers did he score?

12 A box of 'Cleano' now contains $\frac{2}{3}$ extra. Normally it contains 420 g.
How much does it have now?

13 In a sale, a music system has $\frac{3}{7}$ knocked off the price. If it was
originally priced at £392, what does it cost in the sale?

TASK 5.2

M

Change the following improper fractions to mixed numbers.

1 ⊘ ⊘ ⊘ $\frac{8}{3}$ **2** ⊗ ⊗ $\frac{7}{6}$ **3** ⊗ ⊗ ⊗ $\frac{14}{5}$ **4** $\frac{8}{5} = 1\frac{\square}{5}$

5 $\frac{7}{3} = \square\frac{\square}{3}$ **6** $\frac{17}{8} = 2\frac{\square}{8}$ **7** $\frac{9}{2}$ **8** $\frac{13}{3}$

9 $\frac{19}{5}$ **10** $\frac{31}{4}$ **11** $\frac{23}{8}$ **12** $\frac{40}{9}$

E

Change the following mixed numbers to improper fractions.

1 ⊗ ⊗ $1\frac{2}{5}$ **2** ⊛ ⊛ ⊛ $2\frac{5}{8}$ **3** ⊗ ⊗ ⊗ ⊗ $3\frac{5}{6}$ **4** $3\frac{4}{5} = \frac{19}{\square}$

5 $4\frac{2}{3} = \frac{\square}{3}$ **6** $5\frac{3}{4} = \frac{\square}{4}$ **7** $2\frac{7}{8}$ **8** $4\frac{5}{6}$

9 $3\frac{1}{5}$ **10** $9\frac{3}{4}$ **11** $8\frac{2}{3}$ **12** $9\frac{3}{8}$

In the Questions below, change improper fractions to mixed numbers or mixed numbers to improper fractions.

13 $\frac{47}{8}$ **14** $\frac{35}{4}$ **15** $\frac{26}{5}$ **16** $\frac{15}{8}$ **17** $6\frac{2}{3}$ **18** $2\frac{1}{7}$

19 $9\frac{5}{6}$ **20** $\frac{23}{7}$ **21** $\frac{82}{9}$ **22** $\frac{21}{7}$ **23** $4\frac{7}{9}$ **24** $6\frac{5}{8}$

TASK 5.3

M

Work out

1 $\frac{1}{4} + \frac{2}{4}$ **2** $\frac{8}{9} - \frac{7}{9}$ **3** $\frac{8}{11} - \frac{5}{11}$ **4** $\frac{7}{20} + \frac{4}{20}$

5 Tim ate $\frac{3}{7}$ of his pizza and gave $\frac{2}{7}$ of his pizza to his sister who ate it straight away. What total fraction of the pizza has been eaten?

6 Mr. Agg gave $\frac{4}{9}$ of his money to his son and $\frac{4}{9}$ of his money to his daughter. In total, what fraction of his money did he give away?

7 Copy and complete:

a $\frac{2}{7} + \frac{3}{8}$ **b** $\frac{5}{6} - \frac{1}{4}$ **c** $\frac{7}{10} - \frac{2}{9}$

$= \frac{\square}{56} + \frac{\square}{56}$ $= \frac{\square}{12} - \frac{\square}{12}$ $= \frac{\square}{90} - \frac{\square}{\square}$

$= \frac{\square}{56}$ $= \frac{\square}{\square}$ $= \frac{\square}{\square}$

In Questions **8** and **9**, which answer is the odd one out?

8 **a** $\frac{5}{6} - \frac{5}{12}$ **b** $\frac{1}{3} + \frac{1}{4}$ **c** $\frac{2}{3} - \frac{1}{12}$

9 **a** $\frac{1}{4} + \frac{1}{16}$ **b** $\frac{11}{16} - \frac{3}{8}$ **c** $\frac{3}{16} + \frac{5}{8}$

10 Tanya gives $\frac{1}{3}$ of her clothes to her sister and $\frac{1}{10}$ of her clothes to a cousin. What fraction of her clothes did Tanya give away in total?

11 In a class, $\frac{1}{4}$ of the students come by bus and $\frac{3}{5}$ of the students walk. The rest of the students come by car. What fraction of students come by car?

12 Work out

   a $4\frac{1}{2} + 2\frac{2}{3}$ **b** $3\frac{3}{4} + 2\frac{3}{4}$ **c** $7\frac{3}{4} + \frac{7}{10}$ **d** $1\frac{3}{8} + 6\frac{1}{3}$

13 I travel along the road from A to C. What is the total distance I travel?

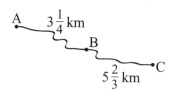

14 Which answer is the odd one out?

   a $3\frac{1}{6} - \frac{3}{4}$ **b** $3\frac{3}{10} - 1\frac{1}{3}$ **c** $4\frac{3}{4} - 2\frac{1}{3}$

15 Joynul has a $1\frac{3}{4}$ metre length of wood. He cuts off $1\frac{1}{10}$ metre of the wood. What length of wood has he got left?

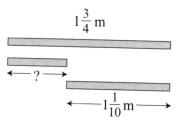

E

Work out (cancel your answers where possible)

  1 $\frac{1}{2}$ of $\frac{1}{3}$ **2** $\frac{1}{3}$ of $\frac{1}{5}$ **3** $\frac{3}{4}$ of $\frac{1}{2}$ **4** $\frac{2}{3}$ of $\frac{3}{5}$

  5 $\frac{1}{4} \times \frac{1}{8}$ **6** $\frac{1}{7} \times \frac{1}{6}$ **7** $\frac{1}{4} \times \frac{2}{7}$ **8** $\frac{3}{5} \times \frac{2}{9}$

  9 $\frac{3}{4} \times 6$ **10** $\frac{5}{6} \times 4$ **11** $\frac{5}{8} \times 10$ **12** $\frac{2}{3} \times 6$

13 Find the area of each of the 3 rooms below:

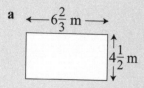

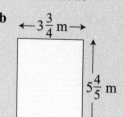

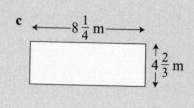

Work out, cancelling where possible:

14 $10 \div \frac{1}{2}$ **15** $6 \div \frac{1}{3}$ **16** $\frac{1}{7} \div \frac{1}{4}$ **17** $\frac{1}{2} \div \frac{1}{3}$

18 $\frac{2}{9} \div \frac{1}{4}$ **19** $\frac{3}{7} \div \frac{2}{3}$ **20** $\frac{2}{11} \div \frac{8}{9}$ **21** $\frac{9}{20} \div \frac{3}{4}$

22 Match each Question to the correct answer (one answer is an odd one out):

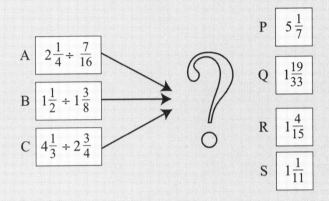

A $2\frac{1}{4} \div \frac{7}{16}$

B $1\frac{1}{2} \div 1\frac{3}{8}$

C $4\frac{1}{3} \div 2\frac{3}{4}$

P $5\frac{1}{7}$

Q $1\frac{19}{33}$

R $1\frac{4}{15}$

S $1\frac{1}{11}$

23 How many whole rods of length $\frac{3}{16}$ m can be cut from a pole of length $\frac{9}{10}$ m ?

NUMBER 4   6

TASK 6.1

M

1 In a survey 73 out of every 100 people said they loved ice cream. Write down the percentage of people who love ice cream.

2 45% of the students in a class said they had been to the cinema in the last month. What percentage of the students had *not* been to the cinema in the last month?

3 68% of men drink alcohol at least once during the week. What percentage of the men do *not* drink alcohol at least once during the week?

4 **a** What percentage of the large square is shaded?

  b What percentage of the large square is *not* shaded?

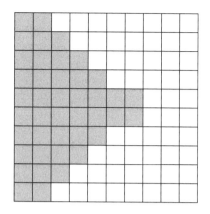

5 53 out of every 100 children walk to school each day.
What percentage of children do *not* walk to school?

E

1 Change these percentages into fractions. Cancel the answers when
possible $\left(\text{example: } 46\% = \frac{46}{100} = \frac{23}{50}\right)$.

  a 17% **b** 20% **c** 29% **d** 12% **e** 25% **f** 60%

  g 24% **h** 35% **i** 88% **j** 32% **k** 9% **l** 95%

2 2% of semi-skimmed milk is fat. What fraction of semi-skimmed milk is fat?

3 Change these fractions into percentages (remember: multiply by 100
unless you can see a quicker way).

  a $\frac{7}{10}$ **b** $\frac{2}{5}$ **c** $\frac{3}{25}$ **d** $\frac{38}{50}$ **e** $\frac{13}{20}$ **f** $\frac{8}{25}$

4 Elmer scored 17 out of 20 for English coursework. What percentage was this?

TASK 6.2

M

1 19 out of 20 pupils in a class go on a school trip. What percentage
of the class go on a school trip?

2 What percentage of these boxes contain:

  a crosses

  b circles

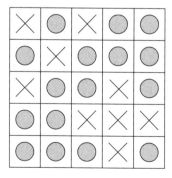

3 **a** Write 19 as a percentage of 50.
    b Write 11 as a percentage of 20.
    c Write 300 as a percentage of 500.

4 In a survey 120 people were asked if they had internet access at home. 96 people said 'yes'. What percentage of the people said they had internet access at home?

5 150 students were asked where their home town was. The findings are shown in this table.
What percentage of the students came from:
  a Wales   **b** The North
  c Ireland   **d** The Midlands

home area	number of students
Wales	45
The South	24
The Midlands	27
The North	36
Scotland	6
Ireland	12
Total	150

E

Use a calculator for the Questions below. Give your answers to the nearest whole number.

1 28 out of 43 young people at a Youth club one evening are male. What percentage of the young people are male?

2 Sunita is given £60 for her birthday. She spends £47 on computer games. What percentage of her birthday money has she got left?

3 What percentage of these letters is the letter 'K'?

O K O K O K
O K O K K K
O K O K O K

4 Tamsin scored 39 out of 47 in a Science test. Peter scored 47 out of 58 in his Science test. Who scored the higher percentage and by how much?

5 The table shows how some of a 30 g serving of sultana bran cereal is made up.
What percentage of the 30 g serving is:

fat	2·6 g
sugars	16 g
salt	0·5 g
saturated fat	1·4 g

  a fat   **b** sugars   **c** salt   **d** saturated fat

6 The population of Glastonbury in Somerset is about 10 000. The population of the UK is about 60 000 000. What percentage of the UK's population live in Glastonbury (give your answer to 2 decimal places)?

38

TASK 6.3

M

1 Find 25% of:
  a 60   b 24   c 44   d 120   e 36

2 Find $33\frac{1}{3}$% of:
  a 15   b 27   c 90   d 54   e 75

3 Find 20% of:
  a 40   b 200   c 140   d 30   e 90

4 Find 15% of:
  a 40   b 140   c 300   d 70   e 10

work out 10% and 5% then add together

5 60% of adults have a mobile phone. If 210 adults were asked, how many would have a mobile phone?

6 Terry earns £260 a week. Each week he gives 5% of his money to charity. How much money does he give each week?

7 Find the odd one out
  a 30% of £30   b 5% of £160   c 25% of £32

E

Use a calculator when needed.

1 Find 1% of:
  a 700   b 250   c 87   d 460   e 6

2 Find 4% of:
  a 300   b 900   c 350   d 75   e 5

3 Find 17·5% of:
  a 400   b 320   c 48   d 680   e 8

4 60 people eat at a restaurant one evening. 55% of these people eat fish. How many people do not eat fish?

5 Find the odd one out
  a 6% of 34   b 14% of 26   c 8% of 45·5

6 The garages of 1600 houses were examined. 23% of the garages had yellow doors. How many garages had yellow doors?

7 Work out, correct to the nearest penny:
  a 13% of £24·20   b 37% of £41·60
  c 19% of £36·14   d 4·8% of £83

TASK 6.4

M

Do not use a calculator.

1 a Increase £40 by 10%.
   c Decrease £50 by 40%.
   b Decrease £70 by 20%.
   d Increase £28 by 75%.

2 Kate earns £340 each week. She is given a pay rise of 5%.
   How much does she now earn each year?

3 A laptop costs £1240. One year later it costs 20% less. How much
   does the laptop cost now?

4 What is the sale price of each item below?

a Sofa £800
   SALE
   30% off

b Dishwasher £480
   SALE
   25% off

c DVD player £60
   SALE
   15% off

5 A car costs £24 000. A year later its price has decreased by 3%.
   How much does the car cost now?

6 Increase £800 by 17·5%.

> Find 10% then 5%
> then 2·5% and add
> them all together

7 VAT is value added tax. This tax is added to the cost of items. VAT
   is usually 17·5%.
   a Find 17·5% of £360.
   b Find the cost of a washing machine which costs £360 + VAT.

E

*Use a calculator when needed. Give answers to the nearest penny
when needed.*

1 a Decrease £70 by 3%.
   c Decrease £264 by 46%.
   b Increase £68 by 2%.
   d Increase £89 by 12%.

2 Carl's caravan is worth £15 500. One year later it is worth 6%
   less. How much is the caravan now worth?

3 A cinema increases its prices by 8%. If a ticket was £6·50, what
   would it cost after the increase?

4 A tin of baked beans costs 42p. Its price increases by 9% over the
   next 12 months. How much will the tin cost now? (remember to
   give your answer to the nearest penny)

5 A new car exhaust costs £88 + VAT. If VAT is 17·5%, work out the total cost of the car exhaust.

6 A new dining table costs £450 + VAT. If VAT is 17·5%, work out the total cost of the dining table.

7 If VAT is 17·5%, find the price including VAT of each of the following:

   a | microwave £126 | **b** | carpet £870 |

   c | digital camera £220 | **d** | kettle £34 |

8 An eternity ring costs £680 + VAT (17·5%).
   a What is the total price of the ring?
   b In the Summer sales, the price of the ring is reduced by 20%. How much does the ring cost in the sales?

TASK 6.5

M

1 Change these percentages into decimals:
   a 47%   **b** 21%   **c** 80%   **d** 36%   **e** 4%   **f** 7%

2 Change these decimals into percentages:
   a 0·59   **b** 0·23   **c** 0·03   **d** 0·3   **e** 0·2   **f** 0·18

3 Match up equivalent fractions, decimals and percentages. (You should find 5 groups of 3 numbers and there is one number on its own)

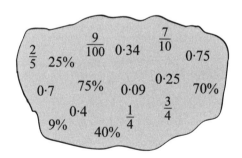

E

Use a calculator when needed. Give answers to the nearest whole number when needed.

1 Ryan buys a mobile for £240 and sells it one year later for £204. What was his percentage loss?

2 Kelly buys a car for £300 and works on it before selling it for £420. What was the percentage profit?

3   A supermarket increases its workforce from 90 people to
    117 people. What is the percentage increase?

4   Find the percentage increase or decrease for each of the following:

   a | original amount = 360 | final amount = 514·8 |

   b | original amount = 672 | final amount = 564·48 |

   c | original amount = 32 | final amount = 62·4 |

5   In 2005, a company makes a profit of £3 million. In 2006, the
    company makes a profit of £4 million. What is the percentage
    increase in the profit?

6   Leanne buys 100 books for £450. She sells each book for £5·40.
    Find the percentage profit Leanne makes on the books.

7   Sam buys 70 scarves at £5 each. He sells 40 of the scarves for £11
    each but fails to sell the other scarves. Find the percentage profit
    he makes.

8   Joe buys a flat for £70 000 and sells it for £85 000.
    Mo buys a house for £192 000 and sells it for £230 000.
    Who makes the larger percentage profit and by how much?

TASK 6.6

M

*Use a calculator when needed. Give answers to the nearest penny
when needed.*

1   Tina invests £8000 in a bank at 5% per annum (year) compound
    interest. How much money will she have in the bank after 2 years?

2   £12 000 is invested at 10% per annum compound interest. How
    much money will there be after 2 years?

3   A motorbike loses 25% of its value every year. Jennifer bought it
    for £720. How much would it be worth after:
    a   2 years   b   3 years

4   Tom buys a guitar for £400. Each year it loses 15% of its value at
    the start of the year. How much would the guitar be worth after:
    a   2 years   b   3 years

5   A bank pays 7% per annum compound interest. How much will the
    following people have in the bank after the number of years stated?
    a   Callum: £5000 after 2 years   b   Megan: £3500 after 2 years
    c   Lauren: £20 000 after 3 years   d   Oliver: £900 after 2 years

42

6 Which of the following will earn more money in 2 years?
    a £4000 at 5·6% p.a. *simple* interest *or*
    b £4000 at 5·5% p.a. compound interest and by how much?

E

1 A bank pays 4% p.a. (per annum) compound interest. Use the *percentage multiplier* 1·04 (100% + 4% = 104%) to find how much money would be in the bank after 3 years if Jack invested £1500.

2 A building society offers 8% p.a. compound interest. Candice puts £560 into the building society.
    a Write down the *percentage multiplier* which could be used to find out how much money is in the building society after 1 year.
    b How much money would be in the building society after 5 years?

3 The population of a small town increases by 14% each year. At the end of year 2001, the town's population was 2600.
Copy and complete the table below, giving your answers to the nearest whole number.

end of year	population
2002	
2003	
2004	
2005	
2006	

4 What is the *percentage multiplier* to find out how much is left after a 21% decrease.

5 A boat is worth £28 000. Its value depreciates (goes down) by 12% of its value each year. How much will the boat be worth after:
    a 3 years   **b** 10 years

6 The value of a house increases by 9% of its value each year. If a house is worth £170 000, how much will it be worth after:
    a 2 years   **b** 7 years   **c** 20 years

> what percentage would you have left after you have taken off 21%?

TASK 6.7

M

1 Copy and complete each sentence below:
    a   The ratio of black to white is ☐ : ☐
    b   The ratio of black to white is ☐ : ☐

2 For each diagram below, write down the ratio of black to white in its simplest form.

a

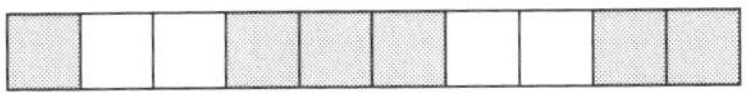

b

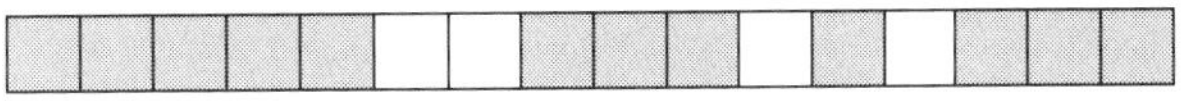

3 Copy the diagrams and colour them in to match the given ratio.

a The ratio of black to white is 2 : 3.

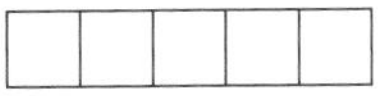

b The ratio of black to white is 2 : 1.

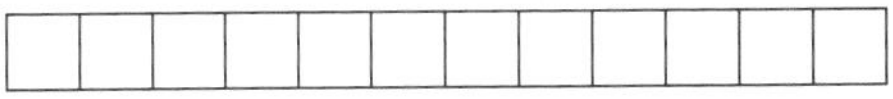

4 In a swimming pool there are 30 people. 20 of the people are male. Find the ratio of males to females. Give the ratio in its simplest form.

5 In a box there are 14 pens and 6 pencils. Find the ratio of pens to pencils in its simplest form.

6 The ratio of boys to girls in a class is 3 : 4. If there are 12 boys, how many girls are there?

7 The ratio of blond haired people to dark haired people is 5 to 2. If there are 6 dark haired people, how many blond haired people are there?

8 Change the following ratios to their simplest form.
a 8 : 10   b 30 : 40   c 12 : 30   d 63 : 27
e 32 : 28   f 12 : 9 : 21   g 50 cm : 4 m   h 25p : £3

E

1 5 lemons cost 95p. What do 3 lemons cost?

2 4 Kiwi fruit cost 84p. What do 6 kiwi fruit cost?

3 7 books cost £42. How much will 9 books cost?

4 8 hats cost £56. How much will 7 hats cost?

5 3 dishwashers cost £1245. What do 5 dishwashers cost?

6 4 calculators cost £23·96. How much will 7 calculators cost?

7 13 people pay £89·70 to visit a castle. How much would 28 people have to pay?

8 Mindy used 550 g of lamb to make a curry for 8 people. How much lamb would she have to use to make curry for 12 people?

9 Cheese kebabs for 4 people need the ingredients below:

220 g	cheese
4	tomatoes
8	pineapple chunks
$\frac{1}{2}$	cucumber

How much of each ingredient is needed for 10 people?

10 The recipe for making 20 biscuits is given below:

> 120 g butter
> 50 g caster sugar
> 175 g flour

How much of each ingredient is needed for 24 biscuits?

TASK 6.8

M

1 a Divide £150 in the ratio 1 : 4   b Divide £60 in the ratio 3 : 2
   c Divide 49 g in the ratio 2 : 5   d Divide 96 kg in the ratio 5 : 3
   e Divide £900 in the ratio 6 : 1 : 3   f Divide 75 litres in the ratio 4 : 5 : 6

2 Todd and Claire receive a total of 30 christmas presents in the ratio
3 : 7. How many presents do each of them receive?

3 A man leaves £12 000 to Carl and Rachel in the ratio 5 : 1. How
much will each person get?

4 The angles p, q and r are in the ratio 7 : 2 : 3.
Find the sizes of angles p, q and r.

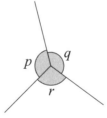

5 There are 45 000 fans at a football match involving Aston Villa and
Birmingham City. The ratio of Aston Villa fans to Birmingham City
fans is 5 : 4. How many Aston Villa fans are at the football match?

E

1 The ratio of boys to girls in a class is 6 : 5. How many girls are
there in the class if there are 18 boys?

2 Paint is mixed by using yellow and blue in the ratio 7 : 2.
   a How much yellow is used if 8 litres of blue are used?
   b How much blue is used if 35 litres of yellow are used?
   c How much yellow and how much blue must be used to make
     72 litres of the paint?

3 Some money is left to Will and Dido in the ratio 9 : 11. If Will
gets £1080, how much will Dido get?

4 Orange squash is diluted with water in the ratio 1 : 7.
  a If 12 ml of orange squash is used, how much water should be added?
  b If 72 ml of water is used, how much orange squash should be added?

5 Des, Simone and Julie earn money in the ratio 3 : 2 : 5. If Des earns £27 000 each year, how much do Simone and Julie each earn?

6 Ginny and Ben have collected 'Warhammer' pieces in the ratio 7 : 4. If Ginny has 63 pieces, how many pieces do they have in *total*?

7 The ratio of weeds to flowers in a garden is 8 : 5. If there are 280 weeds in a garden, how many flowers are there?

8 Ellie, Dan and Lewis own CD's in the ratio 14 : 5 : 9. If Lewis owns 81 CD's, how many CD's do they own in *total*?

SHAPE 2   8

TASK 8.1

M

Use tracing paper if needed.

1 Which shapes are *congruent* to shape A?

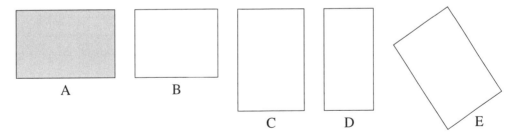

2 Which shapes are congruent to shape P?

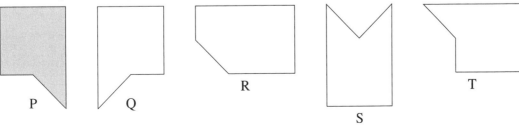

3 Which 2 shapes are congruent?

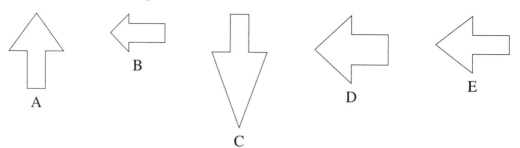

4 Which shapes are congruent to:
  a shape A   **b** shape B
  c shape E   **d** shape F

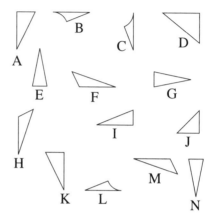

E

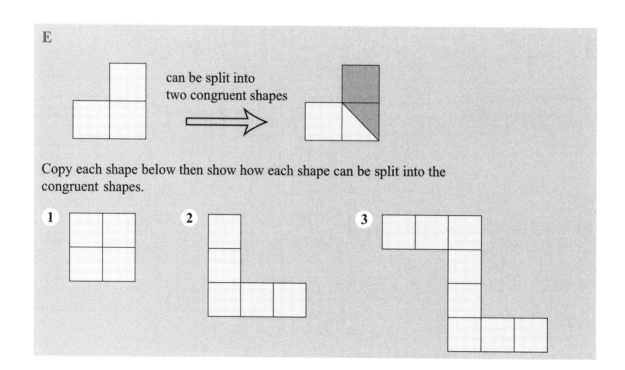

can be split into
two congruent shapes

Copy each shape below then show how each shape can be split into the
congruent shapes.

1   **2**   **3**

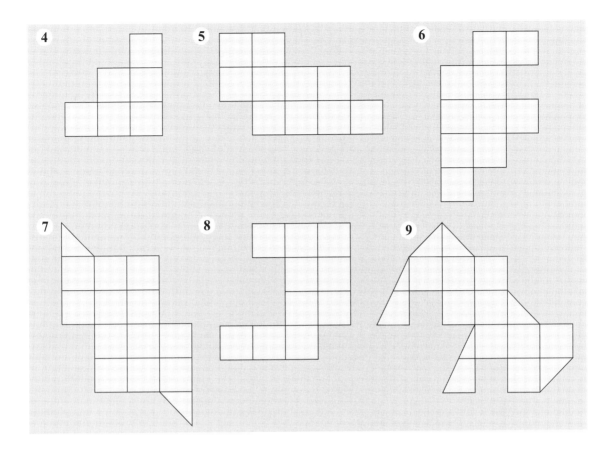

TASK 8.2

M

1 **a** Use this grid to spell out this message.

(4, 1) (3, 4) (1, 3) (4, 5)

(1, 1) (3, 4)

(4, 2) (2, 2) (1, 5)

b Use co-ordinates to write
the word SENSIBLE.

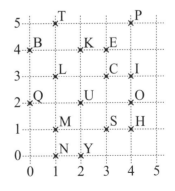

2 Draw a horizontal axis from 0 to 16.
Draw a vertical axis from 0 to 16.
Plot the points below and join them with a ruler in the order given.

(4, 9)	(1, 11)	(3, 8)	(1, 5)	(4, 7)	(6, 5)	(7, 5)	(8, 3)
(9, 5)	(11, 5)	(12, 7)	(15, 9)	(15, 10)	(12, 11)	(9, 11)	(8, 14)
(7, 11)	(6, 11)	(4, 9)					

48

On the same picture plot the points below and join them up with a
ruler in the order given. Do not join the last point in the box above
with the first point in the new box.

$(15, 12)$ $(16, 12)$ $(16, 13)$ $(15, 13)$ $(15, 12)$

$(14, 14)$ $(13, 14)$ $(13, 15)$ $(14, 15)$ $(14, 14)$

$(12, 8)$ $(13, 8)$

Draw a ● at $(13, 10)$ Colour in the shape?

E

1 Draw a horizontal axis from -5 to 12.
Draw a vertical axis from -5 to 12.
Plot the points below and join them with a ruler in the order given.

$(0, -4)$ $(1, 1)$ $(1, -2)$ $(2, -3)$ $(1, -3)$ $(0, -4)$

On the same picture plot the points below and join them up
with a ruler in the order given. Do not join the last point in the
box above with the first point in the new box.

$(3, 6)$ $(3, 3)$ $(5, 5)$ $(6, 7)$ $(6, 10)$

$(-3, 9)$ $(-4, 9)$ $(-4, 10)$ $(-3, 10)$

$(7, -4)$	$(6, -3)$	$(5, -3)$	$(5, -1)$	$(4, 1)$	$(3, 2)$	$(2, 5)$
$(3, 6)$	$(4, 8)$	$(6, 10)$	$(5, 12)$	$(3, 12)$	$(2, 11)$	$(-1, 11)$
$(-3, 10)$	$(-3, 9)$	$(-2, 8)$	$(0, 8)$	$(1, 7)$	$(-1, 2)$	$(-1, -3)$
$(-2, -3)$	$(-3, -4)$	$(7, -4)$				

$(2, 11)$ $(2, 10)$ $(0, 8)$ $(1, 8)$ Colour me in?

2 Draw a horizontal axis from -10 to 8.
Draw a vertical axis from -10 to 8.
Plot the points below and join them with a ruler in the order given.

$(-10, -7)$	$(-9, -6)$	$(-8, -4)$	$(-6, -2)$	$(-4, -2)$	$(-2, -1)$	$(-2, -1)$
$(3, 1)$	$(2, 2)$	$(2, 4)$	$(4, 2)$	$(5, 2)$	$(7, 4)$	$(7, 2)$
$(6, 1)$	$(7, 0)$	$(7, -1)$	$(6, -1)$	$(5, -2)$	$(4, -1)$	$(3, -1)$

On the same picture plot the points below and join them up with a ruler in the order given. Do not join the last point in the box above with the first point in the new box.

$(6, -1)$	$(6, -3)$	$(4, -5)$	$(4, -9)$	$(5, -9)$	$(5, -4)$	$(3, -6)$	$(3, -9)$
$(2, -9)$	$(2, -6)$	$(1, -5)$	$(-1, -5)$	$(-1, -3\frac{1}{2})$	$(-1, -6)$	$(-2, -7)$	
$(-2, -9)$	$(-3, -9)$	$(-3, -6)$	$(-4, -4)$	$(-4, -6)$	$(-5, -7)$	$(-5, -9)$	
$(-4, -9)$	$(-4, -7)$	$(-3, -6)$	$(-4, -4)$	$(-4, -3)$	$(-7, -8)$	$(-9, -8)$	$(-10, -7)$

Colour me in?

TASK 8.3

M

1 Describe the following *translations*. In each case, write down how many units left or right and how many units up or down:

a C to D   **b** B to C
c E to F   **d** A to B
e D to E   **f** B to G
g G to F   **h** F to C

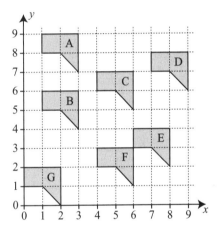

2 Copy the grid opposite and the rectangle A as shown.

a Translate rectangle A 2 units to the right and 2 units up. Label the new rectangle B.
b Translate rectangle B 2 units to the right and 1 unit down. Label the new rectangle C.
c Translate rectangle C 1 unit to the left and 3 units down. Label the new rectangle D.
d Translate rectangle D 4 units to the left and 0 units up. Label the new rectangle E.
e Translate rectangle E 6 units to the right and 1 unit up. Label the new rectangle F.
f Describe the translation that moves rectangle D to rectangle B.
g Describe the translation that moves rectangle E to rectangle C.

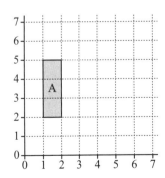

E

1   Use translation vectors to describe the following
    translations.

    a D to C   **b** E to D
    c A to B   **d** E to F
    e D to H   **f** H to F
    g E to B   **h** E to G
    i G to D   **j** F to C

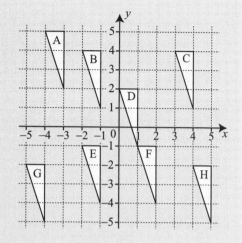

2   Copy the grid opposite and draw shape A
    as shown. Translate shape A by each of the
    translation vectors shown below:

    a $\begin{pmatrix} -4 \\ 1 \end{pmatrix}$ Label new shape B.

    b $\begin{pmatrix} 1 \\ -3 \end{pmatrix}$ Label new shape C.

    c $\begin{pmatrix} -4 \\ -3 \end{pmatrix}$ Label new shape D.

    d $\begin{pmatrix} -1 \\ -5 \end{pmatrix}$ Label new shape E.

    e Use a translation vector to describe the
          translation that moves shape D to E.

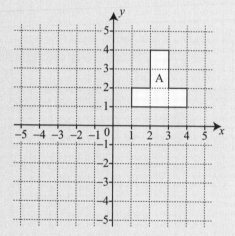

TASK 8.4

M

Draw each shape below and reflect in the mirror line.

1   **2** 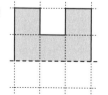   **3**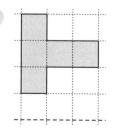

4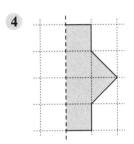

5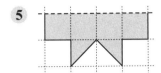

6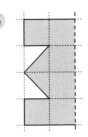

7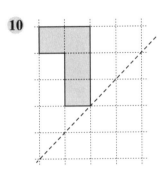

8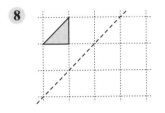

9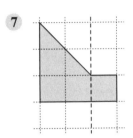

10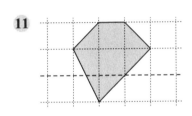

11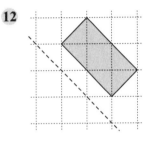

12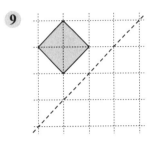

E

1 Copy the grid and shape opposite.

  a Reflect shape A in the *y*-axis.
    Label the image B.

  b Reflect shape B in the *x*-axis.
    Label the image C.

  c Reflect shape C in the line $x = 1$.
    Label the image D.

  d Reflect shape D in the line $y = -1.5$.
    Label the image E.

  e Reflect shape E in the *y*-axis.
    Label the image F.

  f Reflect shape F in the line $y = 2$.
    Label the image G.

  g Shape G reflects back onto shape A.
    Write down the name of the line
    of reflection.

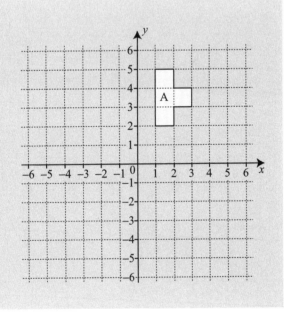

2

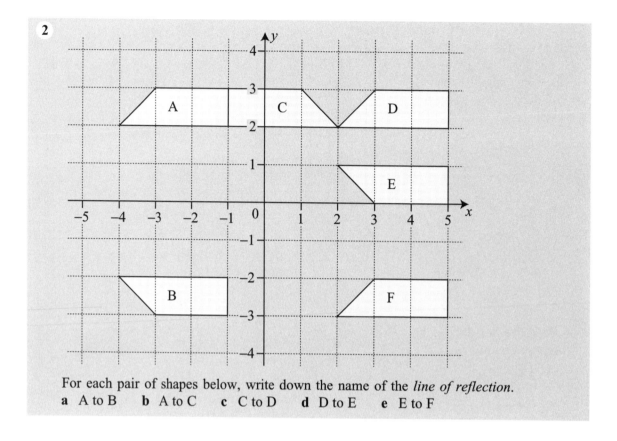

For each pair of shapes below, write down the name of the *line of reflection*.
a A to B **b** A to C **c** C to D **d** D to E **e** E to F

TASK 8.5

M

Use tracing paper.
For each Question, draw the shape and the centre of rotation (C).
Rotate the shape as indicated and draw the image.

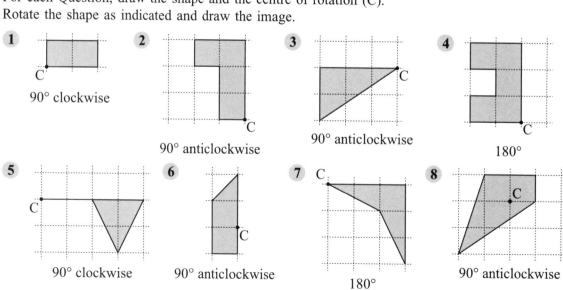

9 Find the co-ordinates of the centres of the following rotations:
  a shape A onto shape B
  b shape B onto shape C
  c shape C onto shape D

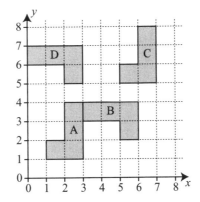

E

Use tracing paper.

1 Describe *fully* the rotation which transforms:
  a triangle A onto triangle B
  b triangle C onto triangle D
  c triangle B onto triangle C

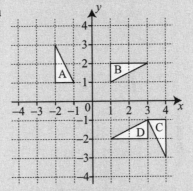

2 a Draw the x axis from −6 to 5.
     Draw the y axis from −6 to 7.
     Draw rectangle A with vertices at
     (2, −2), (3, −2) (3, −5) (2, −5).
  b Rotate rectangle A 90° clockwise about (2, −1). Label the image B.
  c Rotate rectangle B 90° clockwise about (−2, −2). Label the image C.
  d Rotate rectangle C 90° clockwise about the origin. Label the image D.
  e Rotate rectangle D 90° anticlockwise about (−2, 2). Label the image E.
  f Rotate rectangle E 90° clockwise about (3, 2). Label the image F.
  g Describe *fully* the *translation* which transforms rectangle A onto rectangle F.

54

TASK 8.6

M

Enlarge these shapes by the scale factor given. Make sure you leave room
on your page for the enlargement!

1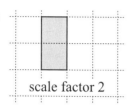
scale factor 2

2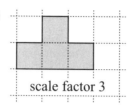
scale factor 3

3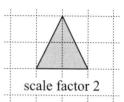
scale factor 2

4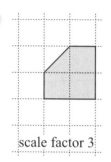
scale factor 3

5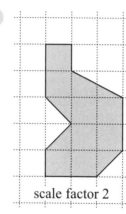
scale factor 2

6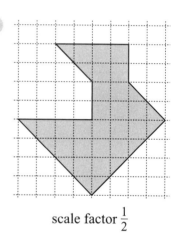
scale factor $\frac{1}{2}$

7 Look at each of the following pairs of diagrams and decide whether or
not one diagram is an enlargement of the other. For each part, write the
scale factor of the enlargement or write 'not an enlargement'.

a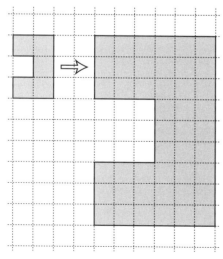

b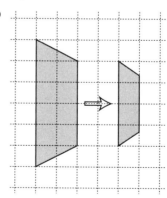

E

For Questions **1** to **3** , copy the diagram and then draw an enlargement using the scale factor and centre of enlargement (C) given.
Leave room for the enlargement!

1

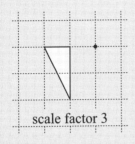

scale factor 3

2

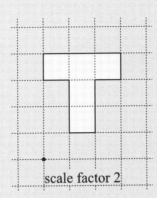

scale factor 2

3

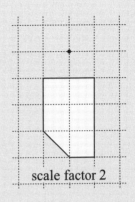

scale factor 2

For Questions **4** and **5** , draw the grid and the 2 shapes then draw broken lines through pairs of points in the new shape and the old shape.
Describe *fully* the enlargement which transforms shape A onto shape B.

4

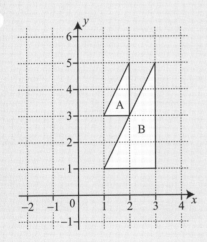

5

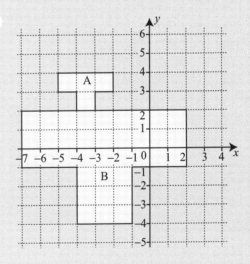

6 **a** Draw the x-axis from -6 to 10.
Draw the y-axis from -3 to 5.
Draw the shape A with vertices at $(-2,2), (-2,3), (-1,3)$, $(-1,4), (-4,4), (-4,3), (-3,3), (-3,2)$.
   b Enlarge shape A by scale factor 3 about $(-6,4)$.
Label the image B.
   c Enlarge shape B by scale factor $\frac{1}{3}$ about $(-3,-2)$.
Label the image C.
   d Enlarge shape C by scale factor $\frac{1}{2}$ about $(0,0)$.
Label the image D.

TASK 8.7

You may use tracing paper.

M

1 Copy the shape and the mirror line.
  a Reflect this shape in the mirror line.
  b Rotate this shape 90° anticlockwise about the point C.

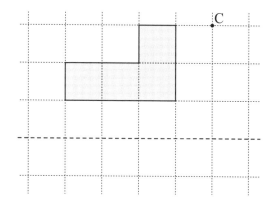

2 Copy the shape.
  a Rotate this shape 90° clockwise about the point C.
  b Translate the image 3 units to the left and 2 units up.

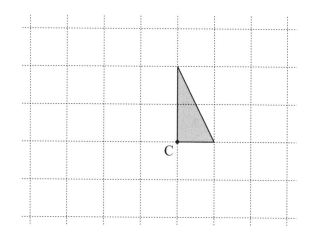

3 **a** Describe *fully* the rotation which moves shape A onto shape B.
  b Describe *fully* the translation which moves shape B onto shape C.
  c Describe *fully* the rotation which moves shape C onto shape A.

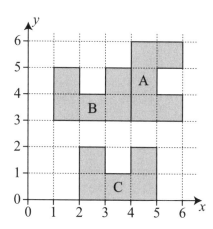

E

1 Describe *fully* the transformation
which moves:
  a triangle A onto triangle B
  b triangle B onto triangle C
  c triangle C onto triangle D
  d triangle D onto triangle E
  e triangle D onto triangle F

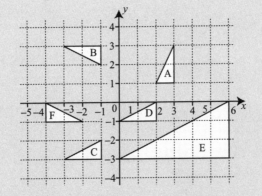

2 **a** Draw the x-axis from -5 to 5.
Draw the y-axis from -6 to 6.
Draw shape A with vertices at $(-2, 2)$, $(-4, 2)$,
$(-4, 4)$, $(-2, 6)$.
  b Enlarge shape A by scale factor $\frac{1}{2}$ about
the origin. Label the image B.
  c Reflect shape B in the line $y = -1$.
Label the image C.
  d Rotate shape C 90° anticlockwise about
$(-2, -2)$. Label the image D.
  e Translate shape D through $\begin{pmatrix} 3 \\ 4 \end{pmatrix}$.
Label the image E.
  f Rotate shape E 90° clockwise about $(2, 2)$.
Label the image F.
  g Describe *fully* the transformation that would
move shape F onto shape C.

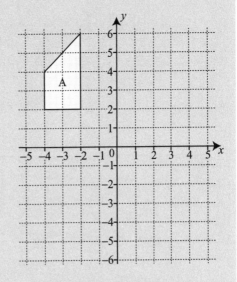

NUMBER 5   9

TASK 9.1

M

1 Work out
  a $\begin{array}{r} 7{\cdot}6 \\ +\,4{\cdot}2 \\ \hline \end{array}$
  b $\begin{array}{r} 2{\cdot}64 \\ +\,5{\cdot}18 \\ \hline \end{array}$
  c $\begin{array}{r} 19{\cdot}7 \\ -\,12{\cdot}4 \\ \hline \end{array}$
  d $\begin{array}{r} 6{\cdot}28 \\ -\,1{\cdot}6 \\ \hline \end{array}$

e 13·0	f 14·68	g 89·53	h 24·7
− 7·4	+ 29·31	− 28·29	8·2
			+ 37·43

2 Write down which sets of numbers below add up to 14.

A $\boxed{3·6 + 7·1 + 3·3}$ B $\boxed{8 + 1·9 + 4·1}$

C $\boxed{5·8 + 6·4 + 2·8}$ D $\boxed{3·12 + 6 + 4·88}$

3 Which answer below is the larger?

A $\boxed{8·12 − 5·6}$ or   B $\boxed{7·36 − 4·74}$

4 Work out the following (Remember to line up the decimal point):
a $4 + 2·17$ b $6·84 + 2·19$ c $51·4 − 17·6$
d $28·6 − 15$ e $49·81 − 16·9$ f $19 − 4·8$

E

1 How much change from a £10 note do you get if you spend:
a £4·81   b £2·64   c £8·21   d £6·72

2 Denise has £20. She spends £3·25 on the bus and £4·83 on lunch. How much money does she have left?

3 Barney can spend up to £1200 on his credit card. He buys a laptop for £895·99, a desk for £104·95 and a computer game for £34·50. How much more money could he spend using his credit card?

4 Which answer below is the smaller?

A $\boxed{5 − 2·42}$ or   B $\boxed{19 − 16·52}$

5

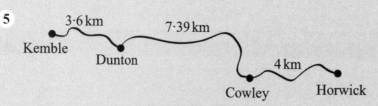

How far is it from Kemble to Horwick?

6 Work out
a $216·4 − 83·26$ b $18·7 + 45 + 13·18$
c $51·8 − 27·27$ d $5·187 − 2·43$

7 Find the perimeter of this pentagon.

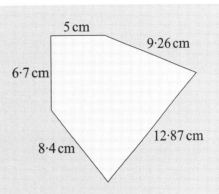

5 cm

9·26 cm

6·7 cm

12·87 cm

8·4 cm

8 Find the *difference* between 46 and 17·48.

9 Colin runs a race in 47·28 seconds. Donna runs the race in 51·1 seconds.
By how many seconds did Colin win the race?

TASK 9.2

M

1 Work out
   a 7·418 × 100   **b** 0·63 × 100   **c** 8·94 × 10   **d** 5·234 × 1000
   e 5·29 × 1000   **f** 0·4 × 100   **g** 7·164 × 10   **h** 8·2 × 1000

2 Copy and fill in the boxes
   a 3·498 × ☐ = 34·98   **b** 0·81 × ☐ = 81   **c** ☐ × 100 = 3·6
   d ☐ × 1000 = 14·6   **e** 0·0913 × ☐ = 91·3   **f** ☐ × 10 = 0·2

3 Work out
   a 6 × 0·1   **b** 29 × 0·01   **c** 0·4 × 0·1   **d** 13 × 0·1
   e 0·71 × 0·1   **f** 48 × 0·01   **g** 631 × 0·01   **h** 0·8 × 0·1

4 Copy and fill in the empty boxes
   a 5·6 × ☐ = 0·56   **b** 384 × ☐ = 3·84   **c** 82 × ☐ = 0·82
   d 3·9 × ☐ = 0·039   **e** ☐ × 0·1 = 0·6   **f** ☐ × 0·01 = 0·34

E

1 For each Question below write 'True' or 'False'
   a 0·6 × 0·3 = 0·18   **b** 0·8 × 0·6 = 0·48
   c 0·4 × 0·08 = 0·032   **d** 8 × 0·05 = 0·4

2 Work out
   a 7 × 0·3   **b** 0·7 × 0·5   **c** 0·9 × 0·3
   d 0·06 × 0·9   **e** 0·08 × 7   **f** $0·4^2$

3 Work out
   a £1·76 × 3   **b** £3·64 × 4   **c** £7·13 × 8

4 Find the total cost of 4 packets of washing powder at £3·28 for each packet.

5 5 people each weigh 68·7 kg. What is their total weight?

6 Which answer below is the correct answer?

   A $1·8 \times 0·7 = 1·26$ or **B** $1·8 \times 0·7 = 12·6$

7 Work out
   a $5·9 \times 0·4$ **b** $26 \times 0·07$ **c** $34 \times 0·03$
   d $0·17 \times 0·5$ **e** $1·3 \times 0·08$ **f** $2·51 \times 0·9$

8 £1 = €1·68. Change £15 into Euros by multiplying by 1·68.

TASK 9.3

M

1 Work out
   a $4\overline{)24·8}$ **b** $6\overline{)12·84}$ **c** $4\overline{)32·20}$
   d $5\overline{)28·0}$ **e** $2\overline{)19·0}$ **f** $8\overline{)13·000}$

2 Divide the following numbers by 4
   a 9·52   **b** 23   **c** 55   **d** 4·5

3 Maggy, Jack, Janet and Wasim go to a rock concert. The total cost of the tickets is £62·60. What is the cost of one ticket?

4 6 cars of beer cost £6·48. How much does one can of beer cost?

5 Work out
   a $11·4 \div 6$ **b** $30·7 \div 5$ **c** $41·92 \div 8$
   d $34·48 \div 4$ **e** $4·83 \div 7$ **f** $0·234 \div 9$

6 A multipack of tins of baked beans costs £1·56. The multipack contains 4 tins of baked beans. A single can of baked beans can be bought for 45p each. Which is the better price for one tin of baked beans and by how much?

E

1 Copy the Questions below and fill in the empty boxes.
   a $13·2 \div 0·4 = 132 \div 4 = \square$
   b $5·84 \div 0·2 = 58·4 \div \square = \square$
   c $7·1 \div 0·02 = 710 \div \square = \square$
   d $15·6 \div 0·02 = \square \div 2 = \square$

2 Work out
   a $1.35 \div 0.3$ b $6.8 \div 0.2$ c $3.36 \div 0.6$
   d $0.192 \div 0.4$ e $0.215 \div 0.05$ f $0.504 \div 0.08$

3 A bottle contains 0·12 litres of medicine. A teaspoon holds 0·005
  litres. How many teaspoons of medicine can be taken from the bottle?

4 Copy and complete the number chains below:

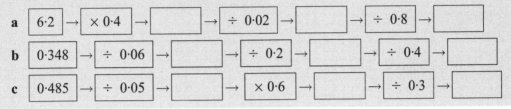

TASK 9.4

M

1 Which of the numbers below are correctly rounded off:
   a 48 → 50 (to nearest 10)   b 152 → 100 (to nearest 100)
   c 124 → 130 (to nearest 10)   d 3817 → 4000 (to nearest 1000)
   e 6·2 → 6 (to nearest whole number) f 42 → 40 (to nearest 10)
   g 5·9 → 5 (to nearest whole number) h 9500 → 9000 (to nearest 1000)
   i 4750 → 4800 (to nearest 100)   j 8·49 → 9 (to nearest whole number)

2 Which of these numbers will round to 7000 when rounded to the nearest 1000:
  7604 6450 6550 6508 6878 6243 6500 7143 7500 7338

3 10 800 people live in the city of Wells (to the nearest 100). Write down
  the least number of people that might live in Wells.

4 Round each of these numbers to the nearest whole number:
   a 7·6   b 14·5   c 0·82   d 52·17   e 14·48

5 75 000 people went on a protest march. If this number had been
  rounded to the nearest 1000, write down the lowest number of people
  that might have been on the protest march.

E

1 Round each of these numbers to the nearest 1 kg:
   a 2·9 kg   b 4·28 kg   c 8·47 kg   d 3·814 kg   e 15·613 kg

2 8·5̲238176 is 9 to the nearest whole number because the first
digit after the decimal point is 5 or more so round up.
Round each of these numbers to the nearest whole number:

   a 3·498173   **b** 6·281365

   c 12·817624   **d** 38·48932

   e 0·724816   **f** 67·5186326

3 Work out these answers *on a calculator* and then round off the answer to the nearest
whole number. Which answer is the odd one out?

   a 431 ÷ 28   **b** 48·3 × 0·3206   **c** 3·9178^2 **d** 624 ÷ 37

4 58 × 81 is roughly 60 × 80 = 4800.
Work out a rough answer to each Question below by rounding each number
to the nearest 10:

   a 89 ÷ 32   **b** 42 × 91   **c** 78 ÷ 11   **d** 59^2

   e 99 × 98   **f** 359 − 72   **g** 19^3 **h** 349 ÷ 68

TASK 9.5

M

1 Which of the numbers below are correctly rounded off to the number
of decimal places shown:

   a 3·68 → 3·6 (to 1 decimal place)   **b** 5·74 → 5·7 (to 1 decimal place)

   c 5·53 → 5·5 (to 1 decimal place)   **d** 8·264 → 8·27 (to 2 decimal places)

   e 6·828 → 6·83 (to 2 decimal places)   **f** 17·614 → 17·6 (to 1 decimal place)

2 Round these numbers to 2 decimal places.

   a 4·814   **b** 0·363   **c** 28·1894   **d** 5·645

3 Which numbers opposite
round to 6·74 (to
2 decimal places)?

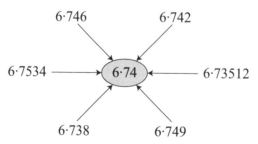

4 Work out these answers *on a calculator* and then round the answers to
the accuracy shown.

   a 4·16 × 2·7 (to 1 decimal place)   **b** 14·6 ÷ 7 (to 2 decimal places)

   c 284 ÷ 31 (to 1 decimal place)   **d** 0·387^2 (to 2 decimal places)

   e 9 ÷ 0·53 (to 3 decimal places)   **f** $\sqrt{29}$ (to 2 decimal places)

   g (7·16 − 3·49)^2 (to 3 decimal places)   **h** 0·72 × 0·81 × 0·3 (to 3 decimal places)

E

1 $5·3 \times 7·8 = 41·34$. Is this likely to be correct?
   $5·3 \times 7·8$ is roughly $5 \times 8 = 40$ so the answer $41·34$ is likely to be correct.
   Write down which answers below are likely to be correct by finding
   sensible **rough** answers. *Do not use a calculator.*
   a $4·8 \times 88 = 422·4$ b $7·9 \times 12·85 = 1015·15$
   c $58·16 - 17·96 = 40·2$ d $8·04^2 = 646·416$
   e $19·9 \times 30·14 = 59·9786$ f $2·06^3 = 874·1816$

2 *Estimate* the area of this rectangle.   14·98 cm

   3·07 cm

3 A shop sells 47 selection boxes for Christmas. Each selection box costs £3·89.
   Estimate how much money the shop receives for the selection boxes.

4 A rectangular room measures 6·2 m by 4·84 m. Carpet costs £19·95
   per square metre. *Estimate* how much it will cost to carpet the room.

5 *Do not use a calculator.*
   Use sensible rough answers to match each Question below to the correct answer:

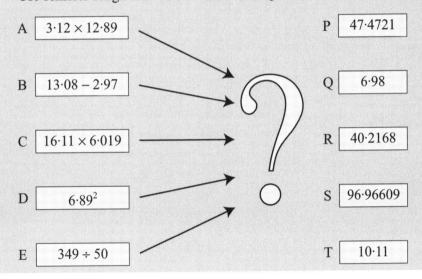

A $3·12 \times 12·89$ P 47·4721

B $13·08 - 2·97$ Q 6·98

C $16·11 \times 6·019$ R 40·2168

D $6·89^2$ S 96·96609

E $349 \div 50$ T 10·11

TASK 9.6

M

Use a calculator.

1 Work out
   a $-9 \div (-3)$ b $-5·6 \times -4·7$ c $-8·1 \times -17$
   d $(2·8 + 3·4) \times 0·9$ e $4·6 \times (6·2 - 3·7)$ f $2·63^2$

2 Work out the following and give your answer *in pounds*.

   a £4·15 × 4   **b** £3·80 × 9   **c** £230·52 ÷ 17

   d 160 × 3p   **e** £7·60 × 12   **f** 14p × 270

3 Each of the calculations below is wrong.
Find the correct answer for each calculation.

   a $\dfrac{48+32}{20}=49\cdot6$ **b** $\dfrac{51-31}{10}=47\cdot9$

   c $\dfrac{50}{25\times10}=20$ **d** $\dfrac{75}{40-20}=-18\cdot125$

4 Work out the following, giving answers to the *nearest whole number*.
Match each calculation to the correct answer.

A $16+4\cdot9-3\cdot17$ P 7

B $3\cdot4\times(5\cdot8-4\cdot25)$ Q 4

C $8\cdot7+\dfrac{2\cdot4}{1\cdot6}$ R 18

D $\dfrac{35\cdot2}{(4\cdot9-0\cdot18)}$ S 10

E $\dfrac{24\cdot63}{2\cdot17+3\cdot42}$ T 3

F $\dfrac{13\cdot8+9\cdot16}{2\cdot4\times3\cdot7}$ U 5

E

1 Write down the fractions shown on the calculator displays below:

   a 3⌐4   **b** 13⌐15   **c** 4⌐2⌐3

2 *Use a calculator* to work out

   a $\dfrac{4}{5}-\dfrac{2}{3}$ **b** $\dfrac{4}{9}\div\dfrac{1}{3}$ **c** $1\frac{1}{5}\times3\frac{2}{7}$ **d** $4\frac{1}{2}\div1\frac{5}{6}$

3 Work out

   a $3\cdot4^2$ **b** $\sqrt{0\cdot49}$ **c** $\sqrt{13\cdot69}$ **d** $(7+9)^2$

   e 8^3 **f** $\sqrt{38\cdot44}$ **g** 4^5 **h** $\sqrt[3]{729}$

4 27 minutes = $\frac{27}{60}$ of an hour = 27 ÷ 60 = 0·45 hours. Write these time intervals *in hours* as decimals.
  a 24 minutes   **b** 33 minutes   **c** 57 minutes
  d 3 hours 15 minutes   **e** 2 hours 6 minutes   **f** 5 hours 42 minutes

5 Work out and give each answer correct to 2 decimal places.
  a $\frac{17·46}{(4·17 + 0·8)}$ **b** $8·623 + 4·9^2$ **c** $2·6^2 \times (9·83 - 1·64)$
  d $\frac{13·6 + 19·5}{2·74}$ **e** $\frac{34·16}{3·6 \times 1·7}$ **f** $\frac{17·2 + 8·16}{8·61 - 2·48}$

TASK 9.7

M

1 Write the numbers below correct to 3 significant figures.
  a 3·168   **b** 5·6163   **c** 41·689   **d** 0·1472
  e 16·594   **f** 61 749   **g** 26 447   **h** 317·58

2 Which numbers below round to 37 200 (to 3 significant figures)?

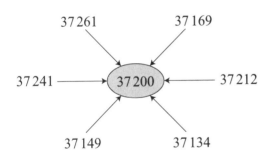

3 Which numbers below are correctly rounded off to 2 significant figures?
  a 5·65 = 5·7   **b** 4189 = 4100
  c 0·0176 = 0·018   **d** 0·0607 = 0·061

4 *Use a calculator* to work out the following, giving each answer to the number of significant figures shown.
  a 64 ÷ 3·7 (3 s.f.)   **b** 20·8 × 11·6 (2 s.f.)
  c (8·14 + 6·5) × 19 (2 s.f.)   **d** $14·6^2$ (3 s.f.)
  e 48 − 12·61 (3 s.f.)   **f** 172 × 486 (2 s.f.)
  g 13·63 ÷ 0·18 (1 s.f.)   **h** $\frac{4·8}{(6·4 + 2·34)}$ (2 s.f.)

66

E

1 *Estimate*, correct to 1 significant figure:

  a 6.9×10.01 **b** $28.03 \div 6.89$ **c** 19.93^2 **d** $\dfrac{4.9 + 15.12}{1.961}$ **e** $\dfrac{9.04^2 + 18.87}{20.07}$

  f $\dfrac{1}{8}$ of £23 998   **g** $\dfrac{3}{4}$ of £79 999   **h** 26% of £12 134   **i** $\dfrac{29.892 + 19.9}{19.94 - 10.103}$

2 Do *not* use a calculator.
  $384 \times 27 = 10\,368$
  Work out
  a $10\,368 \div 27$ **b** $10\,368 \div 384$ **c** 38.4×27

3 Do *not* use a calculator.
  $486 \times 147 = 71\,442$
  Work out
  a $71\,442 \div 147$ **b** 48.6×14.7 **c** 4.86×14.7

4 Do *not* use a calculator.
  $37\,107 \div 63 = 589$
  Work out
  a 589×63 **b** $37\,107 \div 589$ **c** $3710.7 \div 6.3$

ALGEBRA 2   10

TASK 10.1

1 **a** Copy this grid.
  b Draw the line $y = 3$.
  c Draw the line $y = -2$.
  d Draw the line $x = 1$.
  e Write down the co-ordinates where the line $x = 1$ meets the line $y = -2$.

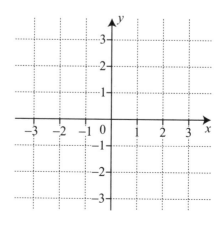

2 **a** Write down the equation of the line which passes through P and R.

   b Write down the equation of the line which passes through S and U.

   c Write down the equation of the line which passes through P and Q.

   d Write down the equation of the line which passes through W, Q and V.

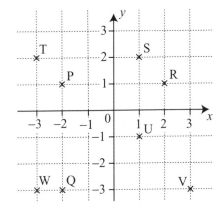

E

For Questions **1** and **2**, you will need to draw axes like these:

1 Copy and complete the table below then draw the straight line $y = 2x + 1$.

x	0	1	2	3
y			5	

2 Copy and complete the table below then draw the straight line $y = 4 - x$.

x	0	1	2	3
y				

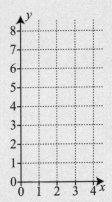

3 Using x-values from 0 to 4, complete a table then draw the straight line $y = 4x$ (make sure you draw the axes big enough).

For Questions **4** and **5**, you will need to draw axes like these:

4 Copy and complete the table below then draw the straight line $y = 2x - 4$.

x	−1	0	1	2	3
y					

5 Copy and complete the table below then draw the straight line $y = 3x + 1$.

x	−2	−1	0	1
y				

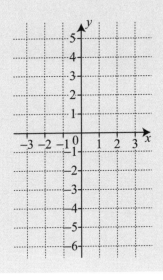

6 Using x-values from -3 to 3, complete a table then draw the straight line $y = 2x + 3$ (make sure you draw the axes big enough).

TASK 10.2

M

1 Find the value of these when $x = -3$:

    a x^2 **b** $x^2 + 2$ **c** $x^2 - 4$ **d** $x^2 + 2x$ **e** $x^2 - x$

For Questions **2** and **3**, you will need to draw axes like these:

2 Complete the table below then draw the curve $y = x^2 + 2$.

x	-3	-2	-1	0	1	2	3
y							

3 Complete the table below then draw the curve $y = x^2 - 1$.

x	-3	-2	-1	0	1	2	3
y							

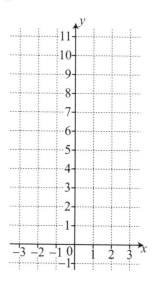

4 **a** Complete the table below for $y = 4x^2$ ($4x^2$ means x^2 then 'multiply by 4').

x	-2	-1	0	1	2
y					

    b Draw an x-axis from -3 to 3 (use $2\,\text{cm}$ for 1 unit) and a y-axis from 0 to 18 (use $1\,\text{cm}$ for 2 units). Draw the curve $y = 4x^2$.

E

For Questions **1** and **2**, you will need to draw axes like those shown on the next page.

1 Complete the table below then draw the curve $y = x^2 + 3x$.

x	-3	-2	-1	0	1	2	3
x^2			1			4	
$+3x$			-3			6	
y			-2			10	

2 Complete the table below then draw
the curve $y = x^2 + 2x - 5$.

x	-3	-2	-1	0	1	2	3
x^2	9						
$+2x$	-6						
-5	-5						
y	-2						

3 Complete the table below then draw $y = x^3 + 2x$.

x	-3	-2	-1	0	1	2	3
x^3							
$+2x$							
y							

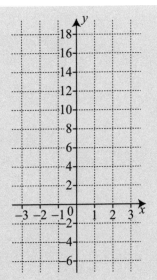

TASK 10.3

M

1 **a** Draw these axes.
   b If $3x + y = 6$, find the value of
     y when $x = \mathbf{0}$.
   c If $3x + y = 6$, find the value of
     x when $y = \mathbf{0}$.
   d Plot 2 points from **b** and **c** and join them up to
     make the straight line $3x + y = 6$.

2 **a** Draw the same axes as in Question **1**.
   b Use $x = 0$ then $y = 0$ to find
     2 points for $2x + 3y = 12$.
   c Draw the straight line $2x + 3y = 12$.

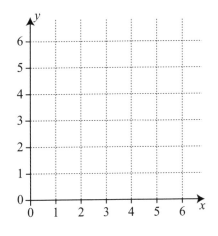

3 **a** Draw an x-axis from $x = 0$ to 8 and a
     y-axis from $y = 0$ to 5.
   b Use the cover-up method with $x = 0$ and
     $y = 0$ to draw $3x + 7y = 21$.

4 **a** Draw an x-axis from $x = 0$ to 6 and a y-axis from $y = 0$ to 10.
   b Use the cover-up method with $x = 0$ and $y = 0$ to draw $8x + 5y = 40$.

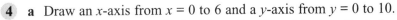

E

1 Use the graph to solve the simultaneous equations below:

a $x + y = 6$
   $2x - y = 6$

b $x - 2y = -6$
   $2x - y = 6$

c $x + y = 6$
   $x - 2y = -6$

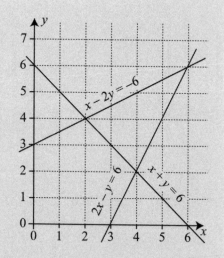

2 a Draw an x-axis from 0 to 7.
     Draw a y-axis from -5 to 5.
   b Use the cover-up method to draw the line $2x + 3y = 12$.
   c Use the cover-up method to draw the line $4x - 2y = 8$.
   d Use your graph to solve the simultaneous equations
     $2x + 3y = 12$
     $4x - 2y = 8$

3 a Draw x and y axes from -2 to 5.
   b Draw the lines $x + y = 4$ and $y = x + 2$.
   c Solve graphically the simultaneous equations
     $x + y = 4$
     $y = x + 2$

TASK 10.4

M

Find the gradient of each line.

1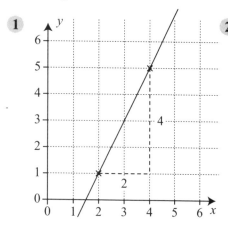

2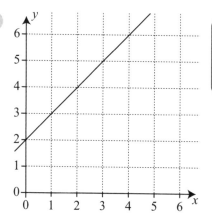

> **Remember:**
> Gradient =
> $\dfrac{\text{vertical distance}}{\text{horizontal distance}}$

3

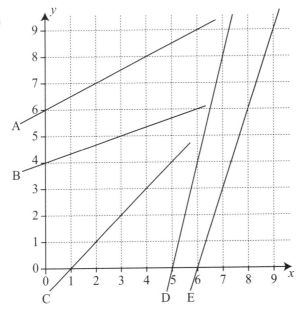

4 Draw a graph to help you if you need to.
Find the gradient of the line joining the points:

a (1, 1) and (3, 5)   **b** (2, 4) and (3, 7)

c (3, 1) and (5, 4)   **d** (1, 0) and (4, 5)

E

1 Find the gradient of each line below:

Remember: a line sloping *downwards* to the right has a negative gradient

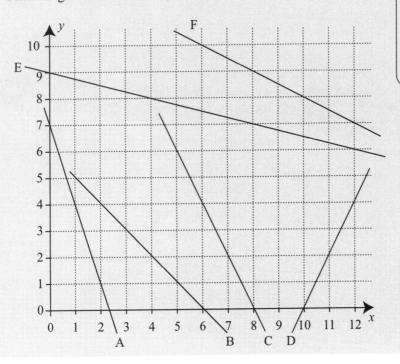

2 Find the gradient of the line joining each pair of points below (draw a graph to help if you need to):

    a $(3, 6)$ and $(5, 2)$ **b** $(1, 4)$ and $(3, 2)$

    c $(0, 5)$ and $(2, 4)$ **d** $(1, 5)$ and $(5, 2)$

3 Find the gradient of each line below (look at the numbers on the axes very carefully):

a

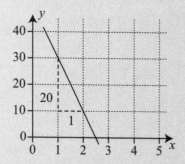

b

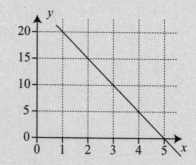

4 Which of the following lines are parallel:

    $y = x + 4$, $y = 4x + 1$, $y = 4 - 3x$,

    $y = 5 + 4x$, $y = 2x + 4$

5 Write down the gradient of these lines

    a $y = 3x + 2$ **b** $y = 8x - 4$ **c** $y = \frac{1}{3}x - 2$

    d $y = 5 - 4x$ **e** $y = 9 + x$

TASK 10.5

M

1 A crowd of 8000 people attended a football match which started at 3 p.m. The graph below shows the number of people who had entered the ground at different times.

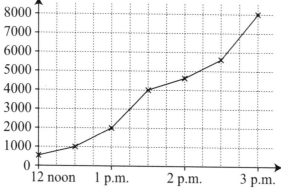

How many people had entered the ground by the following times?

a 1 p.m.   **b** 1:15 p.m.   **c** 2:15 p.m.   **d** 12:45 p.m.

e During which half-hour interval did the *least* number of people enter the ground?

2 The graph opposite shows the temperature during a day:

a What was the temperature at 1 p.m.?

b What was the temperature at 4.30 p.m.?

c At what time was the temperature 20 °C?

d When was the temperature 15 °C?

e When did the temperature start falling?

f How much did it fall by?

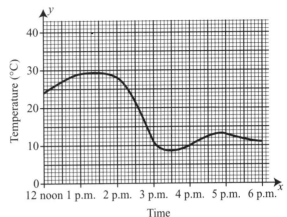

E

1

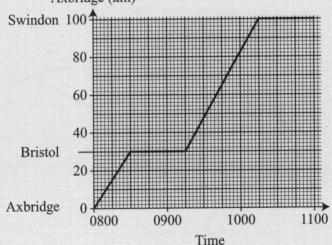

The graph shows the journey of a car from Axbridge to Swindon via Bristol. The vertical axis shows the distance of the car from Axbridge between 0800 and 1100.

a How far was the car from Axbridge at 0815?

b For how long did the car stop at Bristol?

c Find the speed of the car (in km/h) between Axbridge and Bristol.

d Find the speed of the car (in km/h) between Bristol and Swindon.

2 The graph opposite shows a car journey from Manchester.
  a How far from Manchester is the car at 1030?
  b When is the car half way between B and C?
  c At what time is the car 30 km from Manchester?
  d Find the speed (in km/h) of the car from B to C.
  e Find the speed (in km/h) of the car from C to D.

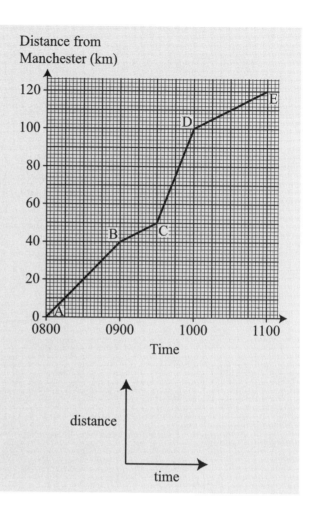

Distance from Manchester (km)

Time

3 Copy these axes and sketch the graph of a car travelling at a steady speed then accelerating rapidly.

distance

time

DATA 1   11

TASK 11.1

M

1 For each statement below, write down whether it is:
  impossible   unlikely   even chance   likely   certain
  a It will snow in January.
  b The next baby born will be a girl.
  c You will go to the toilet within the next week.
  d A friend will give you £10 000 within the next hour.
  e You will get 'heads' if you toss a coin.

2 a Copy this *probability scale.*

| impossible | unlikely | even chance | likely | certain |

0   1

Use an arrow to place each event below on your probability scale:
b You get a 5 if you roll a dice.
c It will be the weekend within the next 7 days.
d You will get a red card if you take one card from a pack of playing cards (26 cards out of 52 are red in a full pack).
e You will wake up in Mexico tomorrow morning.
f You will eat during the next 24 hours.

E

1 Sandeep throws a dice 180 times. The dice lands 72 times on a '2'.
  a How many times should the dice land on a '2' if the dice is fair?
  b From Sandeep's results, find the *relative frequency* of getting a '2'. $\left(\text{relative frequency} = \dfrac{\text{number of times event happens}}{\text{total number of trials}}\right)$
  c Do you think the dice is fair? *Explain* the answer you give.

2 Freddie throws a coin 120 times. The coin lands on 'tails' 58 times.
  a From Freddie's results, find the relative frequency of getting 'tails'.
  b Do you think the coin is fair? *Explain* the answer you give.

3 Jo is throwing an 8-sided dice. She throws the dice 240 times. The table below shows her results.

Score	1	2	3	4	5	6	7	8
Frequency	27	24	36	27	30	27	33	36

  a How many times should each number come up if the dice is fair?
  b From Jo's results, *use a calculator* to find the relative frequency of getting each score (1 up to 8).
  c Do you think the dice is fair? *Explain* the answer you give.

TASK 11.2

M

1 Sue has 15 cards as shown below:

Sue picks a card at random.
What is the probability that she picks the letter:
a C   **b** E   **c** L   **d** S

2 Angus has a bag which contains 7 toffees, 4 mints and 2 chocolates.
Angus picks one of these sweets.
What is the probability that he chooses a:
a mint   **b** mint or toffee   **c** mint or chocolate

3 A bag contains 10 beads. There are 6 blue,
3 red and 1 green.
   a Find the probability of selecting a red bead.
   b 2 more blue beads are put in the bag. Find
     the probability of selecting a blue bead.

4 24 people come for a job interview. 9 of these people wear glasses and
4 of them have contact lenses.
Find the probability that the person chosen for the job:
   a has contact lenses
   b wears glasses
   c does not wear glasses or contact lenses

5 Wendy has six £5 notes, ten £10 notes and four £20 notes in her purse.
If she takes out one note, what is the probability that it will be:
   a a £20 note   **b** a £5 or £10 note   **c** a £50 note
   d She buys a new toaster with a £20 note and a £10 note. If she
     now took out a note, what is the probability that it would be a
     £10 note?

E

   1 A coin is thrown 48 times. How many times would you expect
     it to land on 'heads'?

   2 A dice is thrown 120 times.
     How many times would you expect to get a:
     a 3   **b** 5   **c** 4 or 5   **d** square number

3 This spinner is spun 80 times. How many times should the spinner land on a '0'?

4 The probability of Canning Albion winning a football match is $\frac{2}{3}$. If they play 42 matches in a season, how many matches are they likely to win?

5 The probability of Rob going to the pub on any one day is $\frac{2}{7}$. How many times is he likely to go to the pub in the next fortnight?

6 A bag contains 5 blue balls, 4 red balls and 1 yellow ball.
Brenda takes out one ball at random and then puts it back. If she does this 70 times, how many times would she take out:
a a yellow ball
b a blue ball
c a blue or red ball

7 A bag has only red and blue discs in it. The probability of picking red is $\frac{2}{5}$.
a What is the probability of picking a blue disc?
b Sam picks out 4 red discs without replacing them. What is the smallest number of blue discs that could have been in the bag?
c If Sam picks out a total of 5 red discs without replacing them, what is the smallest number of blue discs that could have been in the bag?

TASK 11.3

M

1 At a café, each person has a main course and a pudding.
One lunchtime the menu is:

main course: Cottage pie or Macaroni cheese
pudding: Trifle or Apple pie

List *all* the different meals that could be ordered.

2 Here are 2 spinners. If I spin both spinners,
I could get a '1' and a '4' (1, 4).

   a List *all* the possible outcomes.

   b How many possible outcomes are there?

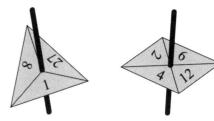

3 Three babies are born. List *all* the boy/girl mixes
(example: B G B   boy, girl, boy).

4 Bart has 4 films (*Antz*, *King Kong*, *Jungle Book* and The *Terminator*).
He only has time to watch two of the films. List *all* the possible
pairs of films that he could watch.

5 Nina has 2 spinners. She spins both spinners
and multiplies the numbers.

For example a '3' and a '4' give 12.

   a Copy and complete this grid to show *all* the
possible outcomes.

   b Find the probability of getting an answer
of 4 when the 2 numbers are multiplied
together.

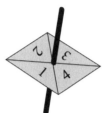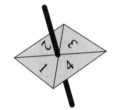

×	1	2	3	4
1				
2				
3				12
4				

E

1 The probability of a bus being late is 0·2. What is the probability of the bus
not being late?

2 The probability of Sean getting up before 11 a.m. on a Saturday morning is $\frac{1}{4}$.

What is the probability of Sean *not* getting up before 11 a.m. on
a Saturday morning?

3 The probability of Karen playing certain sports is shown in the
table below.

hockey	football	badminton	netball
0·5	0·1	*x*	0·2

   a What is the probability of Karen playing hockey or netball?

   b What is the probability of Karen playing badminton?

4 The probability of picking a picture card from a pack of cards is $\frac{3}{13}$.
What is the probability of *not* picking a picture card?

5 If the probability of England winning the next football World Cup is
0·15, what is the probability of England *not* winning the
next World Cup?

6 Don gets to work by either car, bus, tube or bike. The table
shows the probability of each being used.

car	bus	tube	bike
0·25		0·4	0·2

a What is the probability of Don going to work by bus.
b What is the probability of Don going to work by car or bus.
c On his 20 working days in March, how many days would
you expect Don to take the tube?

ALGEBRA 3   12

TASK 12.1

M

In Questions **1** to **8** copy the sequences and write the next *2 numbers*.
What is the rule for each sequence?

1 5, 8, 11, 14, ...   **2** 8, 20, 32, 44, ...

3 44, 39, 34, 29, ...   **4** 3, 4, 6, 9, ...

5 61, 52, 43, 34, ...   **6** 10, 15, 25, 40, ...

7 11, 5, -1, -7, ...   **8** 14, 8, 2, -4, ...

9 You are given the first term of a sequence and the rule. Write down
the first 5 terms of each sequence.
a First term = 7   Rule: add 8
b First term = 61   Rule: subtract 7
c First term = 19   Rule: subtract 5

In Questions **10** to **13** write down the missing numbers.

10 22, 19, ☐, 13, ☐   **11** 5, 12, ☐, 26, ☐

12 -9, -5, ☐, ☐, 7   **13** ☐, 20, 14, 8, ☐

80

14 How many dots are needed for
    a shape 4
    b shape 5

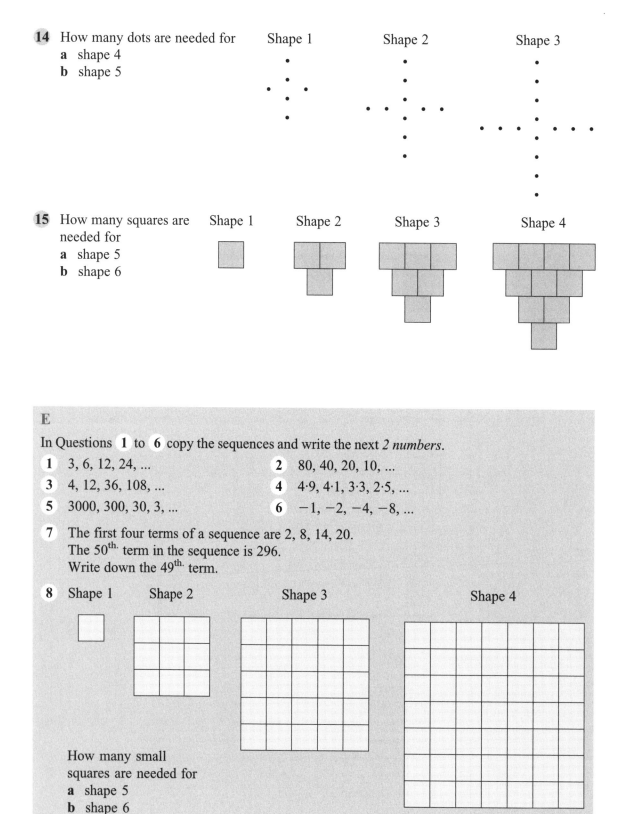

15 How many squares are
    needed for
    a shape 5
    b shape 6

E

In Questions **1** to **6** copy the sequences and write the next *2 numbers*.

1 3, 6, 12, 24, ...

2 80, 40, 20, 10, ...

3 4, 12, 36, 108, ...

4 4·9, 4·1, 3·3, 2·5, ...

5 3000, 300, 30, 3, ...

6 −1, −2, −4, −8, ...

7 The first four terms of a sequence are 2, 8, 14, 20.
    The 50$^{th.}$ term in the sequence is 296.
    Write down the 49$^{th.}$ term.

8 Shape 1   Shape 2   Shape 3   Shape 4

    How many small
    squares are needed for
    a shape 5
    b shape 6

In Questions **9** to **12** find the next *2 numbers* in each sequence (it may help you to work out the 2nd. differences).

9 2, 5, 10, 17, ...

10 0, 3, 8, 15, ...

11 2, 6, 12, 20, ...

12 2, 8, 16, 26, ...

13 The first five terms of a sequence are 1, 2, 4, 8, 16, ...
The 9th. term in the sequence is 512.
Write down the 10th. term of the sequence.

14 Find the next 2 numbers in the sequence below.
Try to explain the pattern.
0, 1, 3, 7, 15, ...

TASK 12.2

M

1 Write down the *term-to-term* rule for each sequence below:
a 3, 12, 48, 192, ...   **b** 53, 45, 37, 29, ...
c 9, 6·5, 4, 1·5, ...   **d** 2, 5, 14, 41, 122, ...

2 The $n^{th.}$ term of a sequence is given by the formula $n^{th.}$ term = $2n + 1$.
Use values of n from 1 to 5 to write down the first 5 terms of the sequence.

3 Use each $n^{th.}$ term formula below to find the first 5 terms of each sequence.
a $n^{th.}$ term = $3n + 5$ **b** $n^{th.}$ term = $4n - 1$ **c** $n^{th.}$ term = $2n + 7$

4 Here is a sequence: 5, 8, 11, 14, ...
The 1st. difference is +3.
Copy and complete the table which has a row for '$3n$'.
Copy and complete: 'The $n^{th.}$ term of the sequence is $3n +$ ☐'

Position n	1	2	3	4
term	5	8	11	14
$3n$	3			12

5 Use the tables below to help you find the $n^{th.}$ term of each sequence.

a Sequence 2, 7, 12, 17, ...

Position n	1	2	3	4
term	2	7	12	17
$5n$	5	10	15	20

$n^{th.}$ term = ☐

b Sequence 7, 11, 15, 19, ...

Position n	1	2	3	4
term	7	11	15	19
$4n$	4	8	12	16

$n^{th.}$ term = ☐

6 Match up each sequence to the correct $n^{\text{th.}}$ term formula.

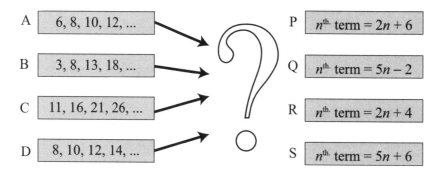

A | 6, 8, 10, 12, ...

B | 3, 8, 13, 18, ...

C | 11, 16, 21, 26, ...

D | 8, 10, 12, 14, ...

P | $n^{\text{th.}}$ term $= 2n + 6$

Q | $n^{\text{th.}}$ term $= 5n - 2$

R | $n^{\text{th.}}$ term $= 2n + 4$

S | $n^{\text{th.}}$ term $= 5n + 6$

7 Find the $n^{\text{th.}}$ term of each sequence below (make a table like Question **5** if you need to).

a 7, 10, 13, 16, ...
b 9, 16, 23, 30, ...
c 1, 10, 19, 26, ...
d 6, 14, 22, 30, ...
e 30, 26, 22, 18, ...
f 18, 13, 8, 3, ...
g 8, 12, 16, 20, ...
h 22, 19, 16, 13, ...

E

1 Here is a sequence of shapes made from squares.
Let n = shape number and w = number of white squares.

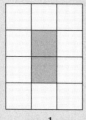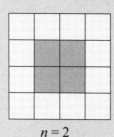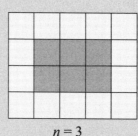

$n = 1$
$w = 10$

$n = 2$
$w = 12$

$n = 3$
$w = 14$

a Draw the next shape in the sequence.
b How many white squares are in shape number 4?
c Copy and complete the table of values.
The 1st. difference is +2.

n	1	2	3	4
w	10	12	14	

d Find a formula for the number of white squares (w) for the shape number n. Use values of n to *check* if your formula is correct.
e Use your formula to find out how many white squares are in shape number 50.

2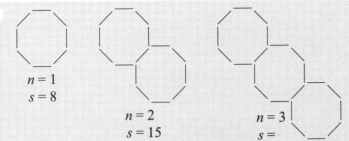

$n = 1$
$s = 8$

$n = 2$
$s = 15$

$n = 3$
$s =$

a Draw the next shape in the sequence.
b Let n = shape number and s = number of sticks.
   Complete a table of values for n and s.
c Use the table and $1^{\text{st.}}$ difference to find a formula for the number of sticks (s)
   for the shape number n.
   Use values of n to check if each formula is correct.
d Use the formula to find out how many sticks are in shape number 40.

3 Repeat Question **2** for the sequence below:

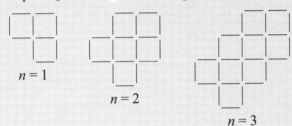

$n = 1$

$n = 2$

$n = 3$

TASK 12.3

M

1 Solve these equations:
   a $n + 3 = 8$ **b** $n + 8 = 15$ **c** $n - 3 = 6$ **d** $n - 7 = 9$
   e $n + 12 = 43$ **f** $x - 9 = 19$ **g** $x - 24 = 18$ **h** $x + 37 = 60$
   i $x + 26 = 41$ **j** $x - 38 = 14$ **k** $n - 49 = 28$ **l** $n + 58 = 73$

2 Ian thinks of a number and then subtracts 14. If the answer is 25,
   what number did Ian think of?

3 Solve
   a $6 \times n = 30$ **b** $6n = 24$ **c** $3n = 21$ **d** $n - 14 = 21$
   e $n \div 3 = 5$ **f** $\frac{n}{4} = 2$ **g** $\frac{x}{10} = 6$ **h** $\frac{x}{7} = 4$
   i $\frac{x}{5} = 8$ **j** $8x = 48$ **k** $x - 34 = 28$ **l** $9x = 54$

4 Find the value of x in this rectangle.

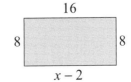

E

1 Solve these equations:
   a $n + 3 = 1$ **b** $n + 2 = 1$ **c** $n + 5 = 3$ **d** $n - 3 = -6$
   e $n + 8 = 0$ **f** $3n = -6$ **g** $10x = -8$ **h** $-5x = -20$
   i $4n = -28$ **j** $n \div 3 = -4$ **k** $\frac{x}{5} = -5$ **l** $\frac{x}{7} = -3$

2 Pat thinks of a number and then adds 10. If the answer is 5, what number did Pat think of?

3 Teresa doubles a number and gets the answer 9. What was the number?

4 Solve
   a $2x = 1$ **b** $2x = 5$ **c** $3n = 7$ **d** $5n = 4$
   e $2n = -3$ **f** $5x = 7$ **g** $7x = -4$ **h** $3n = -11$

> **Remember:**
> if $3x = 2$ then
> $x = \frac{2}{3}$

TASK 12.4

M

In Questions **1** to **3**, copy and fill the empty boxes.

1 $\boxed{3n} + 2 = 20$
     $\boxed{3n} = 18$
     $n = \boxed{}$

2 $\boxed{5n} + 6 = 26$
     $\boxed{5n} = \boxed{}$
     $n = \boxed{}$

3 $\boxed{4x} - 7 = 1$
     $\boxed{4x} = \boxed{}$
     $x = \boxed{}$

Solve these equations:

4 $2n + 1 = 9$ **5** $3n + 8 = 17$ **6** $6n + 4 = 16$
7 $3n + 5 = 20$ **8** $4x + 6 = 18$ **9** $5x - 2 = 18$
10 $8x - 1 = 23$ **11** $6x - 7 = 23$ **12** $3n - 8 = 19$

13 Find the value of x in this rectangle.

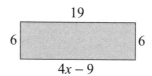

Solve:

14 $8x + 2 = 50$ **15** $9x - 8 = 55$ **16** $6n - 10 = 32$
17 $6n + 8 = 62$ **18** $7x - 14 = 35$ **19** $39 = 3x + 9$
20 $34 = 5x - 6$ **21** $8n - 26 = 30$ **22** $29 = 9x - 7$

E

In Questions **1** to **3**, copy and fill the empty boxes.

1 $\boxed{3n} + 4 = 6$

$\boxed{3n} = 2$

$n = \dfrac{2}{\boxed{}}$

2 $\boxed{5n} + 6 = 9$

$\boxed{5n} = \boxed{}$

$n = \dfrac{\boxed{}}{\boxed{}}$

3 $10 = 18 \boxed{+2n}$

$\boxed{} = 2n$

$\boxed{} = n$

Solve these equations:

4 $5n + 4 = 7$

5 $2x + 5 = 10$

6 $4x + 7 = 10$

7 $8x + 5 = 10$

8 $3n + 6 = 13$

9 $2n - 9 = 2$

10 $4n - 2 = 1$

11 $9x - 5 = 2$

12 $10x + 14 = 37$

13 If we multiply a number by 5 and then add 3, the answer is 4. What is the number?

14 If we multiply a number by 7 and then subtract 2, the answer is 3. What is the number?

Solve:

15 $3n + 8 = 6$

16 $5n + 6 = 4$

17 $6x + 7 = 6$

18 $8 = 20 + 4x$

19 $15 = 27 + 3x$

20 $8x - 2 = -5$

TASK 12.5

M

In Questions **1** to **3**, copy and fill the empty boxes.

1 $4(n + 2) = 20$

$4n + \boxed{8} = 20$

$4n = \boxed{}$

$n = \boxed{}$

2 $3(2n + 3) = 15$

$6n + \boxed{} = 15$

$6n = \boxed{}$

$n = \boxed{}$

3 $2(2n - 3) = 14$

$\boxed{} - 6 = 14$

$\boxed{} = 20$

$n = \boxed{}$

Solve these equations:

4 $3(n + 1) = 15$

5 $5(n + 4) = 30$

6 $10(n - 4) = 70$

7 $4(n - 3) = 24$

8 $6(x - 5) = 18$

9 $2(2x + 3) = 14$

10 $5(2x - 1) = 25$

11 $3(2n + 7) = 27$

12 $6(n - 4) = 36$

13 I think of a number. I add 9 onto the number then multiply the answer by 3. This gives 36. What was the number I started with?

Solve:

14 $2(2x - 4) = 12$

15 $4(2n + 5) = 52$

16 $2(3n - 5) = 20$

17 $3(3x + 6) = 54$

18 $5(2n - 6) = 40$

19 $4(2x - 7) = 20$

E

In Questions **1** to **3**, copy and fill the empty boxes.

1　$2(n + 5) = 11$

　　□ $+ 10 = 11$

　　　□ $= 1$

　　　　$n = \dfrac{□}{□}$

2　$3(2n + 3) = 3$

　　$6n +$ □ $= 3$

　　　$6n = $ □

　　　　$n = $ □

3　$5(x + 2) = 8$

　　$5x + $ □ $= 8$

　　　$5x = $ □

　　　　$x = \dfrac{□}{□}$

Solve these equations:

4　$2(n + 3) = 3$　　　**5**　$5(x + 2) = 6$　　　**6**　$3(2x - 1) = 2$

7　$5(2x + 3) = 18$　　**8**　$4(n - 2) = 11$　　**9**　$6 = 3(n + 4)$

10　$18 = 2(6 - x)$　　**11**　$70 = 10(2 - 5x)$　　**12**　$3(2n + 5) = 14$

TASK 12.6

M

Find the value of n in Questions **1** to **4**:

1

2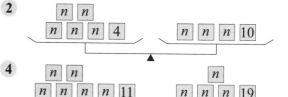

3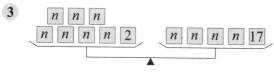

4

Solve these equations:

5　$5n + 9 = 4n + 18$　　　　　　**6**　$8n + 7 = 3n + 2$

7　$7x + 6 = 3x + 18$　　　　　　**8**　$9x + 1 = 2x + 43$

In Questions **9** and **10**, copy and fill the empty boxes.

9　$6n - 3 = 2n + 17$

　　$4n - 3 = 17$

　　　$4n = 20$

　　　　$n = $ □

10　$8x - 9 = 3x + 26$

　　□ $- 9 = 26$

　　　□ $= 35$

　　　$x = $ □

Solve these equations:

11　$5n - 3 = 2n + 18$　　　　　**12**　$8n - 3 = 2n + 27$

13　$4n - 9 = 3n + 7$　　　　　　**14**　$9x - 6 = 6x + 18$

15　$6x + 12 = 2x + 20$　　　　　**16**　$8x - 10 = 5x + 20$

17　$5x - 7 = x + 29$　　　　　　**18**　$4n + 13 = 2n + 25$

19　$7n - 8 = 3n + 28$　　　　　　**20**　$10x - 6 = 7x + 15$

E

In Questions **1** to **3**, copy and fill the empty boxes.

1 $5x + 12 = 2x + 10$
$3x + 12 = 10$
$3x = \boxed{}$
$x = \dfrac{\boxed{}}{\boxed{}}$

2 $3(2x + 4) = 4(x + 6)$
$6x + \boxed{} = \boxed{} + 24$
$2x = \boxed{}$
$x = \boxed{}$

3 $5n - 2 = 3n - 8$
$2n - 2 = -8$
$2n = \boxed{}$
$n = \boxed{}$

Solve these equations:

4 $4x + 3 = x + 4$

5 $7n + 4 = 2n + 8$

6 $5n + 3 = 27 - n$

7 $3x + 9 = 44 - 2x$

8 $6x + 10 = 4x + 6$

9 $5x + 19 = 11 - 3x$

10 This is an *isosceles* triangle.
Find the value of x.

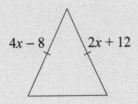

$4x - 8$ $2x + 12$

Solve:

11 $4(2x + 1) = 2(3x + 5)$

12 $5(3x + 4) = 4(3x + 20)$

13 $2(4x - 3) = 5(x + 6)$

14 $4(3n - 1) = 2(5n + 7)$

15 $5(2n + 4) = 2(4n + 3)$

16 $3(3x + 2) + 5(x + 4) = 54$

TASK 12.7

M

Solve these equations:

1 $3x + 7 = 31$

2 $\dfrac{x}{3} + 7 = 10$

3 $\dfrac{x}{4} + 9 = 15$

4 $\dfrac{x}{8} - 5 = 1$

5 $5x - 10 = 30$

6 $\dfrac{x}{5} - 2 = 8$

7 **a** Write down an equation using the angles.
b Find x.
c Write down the actual value of each angle in this triangle.

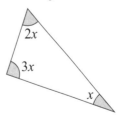

$2x$
$3x$
x

8 The area of this rectangle is 60 cm^2.
a Write down an equation involving x.
b Find x.

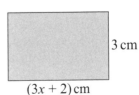

3 cm

$(3x + 2)$ cm

9 The perimeter of the rectangle opposite is 50 cm.
 a Write down an equation using the perimeter.
 b Find x.
 c Write down the actual length and width of the rectangle.

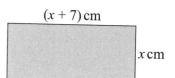

$(x + 7)\,$cm

$x\,$cm

Solve these equations:

10 $\dfrac{x}{7} - 4 = 4$

11 $\dfrac{x - 4}{7} = 4$

12 $\dfrac{x + 9}{4} = 6$

13 $4(2x + 1) = 28$

14 $\dfrac{x}{5} - 3 = 2$

15 $\dfrac{x - 8}{6} = 5$

E

Solve these equations:

1 $5(2x - 3) = 3(x + 2)$

2 $\dfrac{x + 7}{6} = 3$

3 $\dfrac{x}{4} + 6 = 3$

4 $5n + 10 = 3n + 2$

5 $2(4n - 1) = 3(2n + 5)$

6 $\dfrac{3x + 5}{2} = 3$

7 $\dfrac{30}{x} = 5$

8 $8 = \dfrac{56}{x}$

9 $\dfrac{2n + 16}{5} = 2$

10 $7 - 2x = 3x + 3$

11 **a** Write down an equation using
 the angles.
 b Find x.
 c Write down the actual value of each
 angle in this quadrilateral.

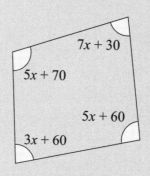

$7x + 30$

$5x + 70$

$5x + 60$

$3x + 60$

> **Remember:**
> the angles in a
> quadrilateral
> add up to 360°.

12 The length of a rectangle is 8 cm more than its width. If its perimeter is 44 cm,
 find its width.

13 Hannah has 3 times as much money as Joe. Hannah spends £24 on a new blouse.
 She now has £30 left. How much money has Joe got?

14 This is an *isosceles* triangle.
 a Find the value of x.
 b Find the perimeter of the triangle.

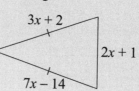

$3x + 2$

$2x + 1$

$7x - 14$

15 The areas of each rectangle are equal
   (all lengths are measured in cm).
   a Find the value of x.
   b Find the area of one of the rectangles.

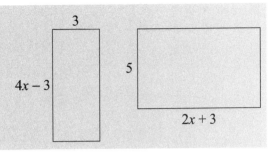

$4x - 3$

3

5

$2x + 3$

TASK 12.8

M

1 The area of this rectangle is 25 cm^2.
   Copy and complete this table to find x to 1 decimal place.

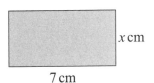

x cm

7 cm

trial	calculation	too large or too small?
$x = 3$	$7 \times 3 \ = ...$	too small
$x = 4$	$7 \times 4 \ = ...$	too large
$x = 3{\cdot}5$	$7 \times 3{\cdot}5 = ...$	too ...
$x = 3{\cdot}6$	$7 \times 3{\cdot}6 = ...$	too ...

So $x = ...$ to 1 decimal place.

2 The area of this square is 85 cm^2.
   Area $= x \times x = x^2$
   We want $x^2 = 85$

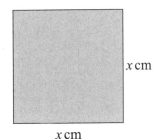

x cm

x cm

Copy and complete this table to find x to 1 decimal place.

trial	calculation	too large or too small?
$x = 10$	$10 \times 10 \ = 100$	too large
$x = 9$	$9 \times 9 \ = ...$	too ...
$x = 9{\cdot}5$	$9{\cdot}5 \times 9{\cdot}5 = ...$	too ...
$x = 9{\cdot}2$	$9{\cdot}2 \times 9{\cdot}2 = ...$	too ...
$x = 9{\cdot}3$	$9{\cdot}3 \times 9{\cdot}3 = ...$	too ...

So $x = ...$ to 1 decimal place.

3 The volume of this cube is 250 cm³.
Use trial and improvement to find x to 1 decimal place.

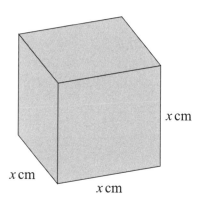

x cm

x cm

x cm

E

1 The area of this rectangle is 42 cm². Use trial and improvement to find x to 2 decimal places.
Show all your working out.

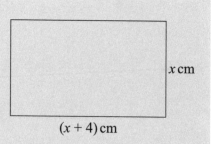

x cm

$(x + 4)$ cm

2 Solve these equations by trial and improvement. Give each answer to 2 decimal places. *Show all your working out.*
  a $x^2 - 3x = 15$ **b** $x^3 + x = 788$ **c** $x^3 - 5x = 267$

DATA 2   13

TASK 13.1

M

1 Write the following numbers in order of size then write down the median.
  7   2   18   4   6   14   12   19   14

2 Find the mode of each set of numbers below:
  a 3 7 1 4 5 3 5 2 3 4 9 3 6
  b 5 4 6 2 4 6 1 6 2 8 3 2

3 There are 5 people aged
  23, 48, 46, 9 and 58 in a Rolls Royce.
  There are 4 people aged
  57, 28, 4 and 31 in a Citroen Saxo.
  Which car contains the larger range of ages?

4 10 people weigh the following (in kg):
65 85 70 65 80 95 70 85 90 95
Find their mean average weight.

For each set of numbers below, find
 a the mean
 b the median
 c the mode and
 d the range.

5 6 10 9 3 16 10 2

6 8 11 4 8 15 4 16 5 10

7 6 3 9 9 2 7

8 The number of children in each of 20 families is shown below:
2 3 0 1 4
1 2 1 2 0
3 2 2 1 5
2 1 2 0 2
Use a calculator to work out the mean average number of children
in each family.

9 The ages of the members of a football team are:
19 27 22 21 24 33 29 26 22 18 31
Two players are 'sent off' in a match. They are the 29 year-old
and the 18 year-old.
Find the mean age of the players left on the pitch.

E

 1 Seven people score the following marks in a test:
30 40 40 40 45 45 96
Find **a** the mean
   b the median
   c Which average best describes these marks? *Explain why.*

 2 In a shooting match, Rose scores:
8, 9, 9, 9, 10, 9, 9, 9, 9, 10
Find **a** the mode
   b the mean
   c Which average best describes these scores, the mode or
    the mean? *Explain why.*

 3 ☐ ☐4☐ ☐ ☐9☐ ☐
Ross has 5 cards.
The 5 cards have a mean of 7, a median of 7 and a range of 13.
What are the 5 numbers on the cards?

4 The mean average age of 6 people is 37.
What is the total of all their ages?

5 The mean weight of 11 people is 63 kg.
 a What is the total weight of all 11 people?
 b One person of weight 83 kg leaves the group.
   Find the mean weight of the remaining 10 people.

6 The mean average salary of 7 people is £26 500.
Gemma joins the group. If she earns £32 100,
what is the mean average salary of all 8 people?

7 Which kind of average is the most sensible to use to show the
amount of money earned by each person in the UK. *Explain why.*

TASK 13.2

M

1 The bar chart shows how many goals, Towton United and Hotley Albion,
scored in each of the years shown.

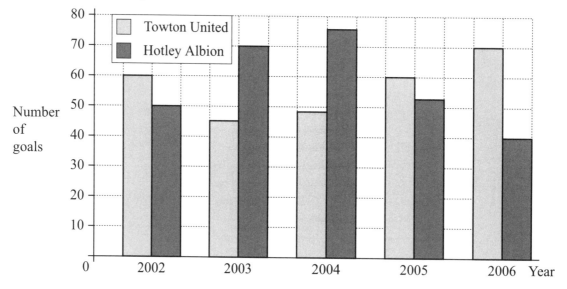

How many goals did Towton United score in:
a 2002   b 2003   c 2006
d In which year did Hotley Albion score 76 goals?
e In which years did Towton United score the same number of goals?
f How many *more* goals did Hotley Albion score than Towton United in 2004?
g How many *more* goals did Towton United score than Hotley Albion in 2006?
h Which team scored more goals during *all* 5 years and how many
more did they score?

2 In an accident 'blackspot', there were 8 accidents in 2001, 10 accidents in 2002, 6 accidents in 2003, 14 accidents in 2004 and 4 accidents in 2005. Copy and complete the pictogram below:

2001	
2002	
2003	⊢⊣ ⊢
2004	
2005	

⊢——⊣ means 4 accidents

3 The graph below shows how many males and females work at an electronics firm called 'Manucomp.'

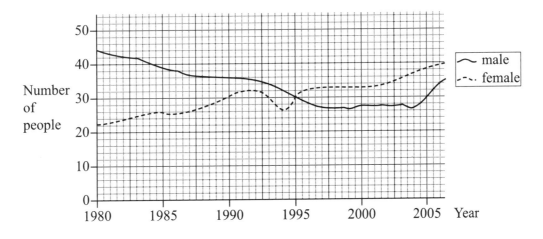

How many female workers were there in:

a 1985   **b** 2000   **c** 2005

d In what year were there the same number of male and female workers?

e How many *more* female workers than male workers were there in the year 2000?

f What was the rise in female workers between 1980 and 2005?

E

1 This stem and leaf diagram shows how much money was raised by some children on a sponsored 'silence.'

   a Write down the median amount of money.

   b What is the range for these amounts of money?

Stem	Leaf
1	7 9
2	4 4 5 8 9 9
3	2 6 6
4	3 8 8 8
5	1 4

Key 2|4 = £24

2 The weights of 22 people were recorded to the nearest kg.

   64 71 63 78 82 49 71 65 74 78 53

   58 82 66 65 71 87 65 53 72 68 81

   a Show this data on a stem and leaf diagram.

   b Write down the range of this data.

3 The heights of the players in two hockey teams, the Tampton Trojans and Mallow Town, are shown in the back-to-back stem and leaf diagram.

The Tampton Trojans		Mallow Town
	15	6
9 3	16	1 8 8
8 5 5 2 1	17	2 4 7 7
4 4 3	18	3
6	19	0 2

Key 2|17 = 172   Key 18|3 = 183

   a Find the median and range for Mallow Town.

   b Find the median and range for the Tampton Trojans.

   c Write a sentence to compare the heights of the players in each hockey team (use the median and range).

TASK 13.3

M

1 The table below shows how a group of people get to work each morning.

   a Find the total frequency.

   b Work out the angle for each person to help draw a pie chart. (i.e. 360° ÷ 'total frequency')

   c Work out the angle for each type of transport and draw a pie chart.

type of transport	frequency (number of people)
bus	30
car	10
tube	25
on foot	15
bike	10

In Questions **2** and **3**, work out the angle for each item and draw a pie chart.

2 Favourite type of film

film	frequency
adventure	6
comedy	18
horror	7
romance	2
cartoon	12

3 Favourite colour

colour	frequency
blue	23
green	8
red	28
yellow	41
purple	4
other	16

E

1 300 people were asked what their favourite hot drink is.
The pie chart shows the findings.
How many people chose:
a coffee   **b** others   **c** tea

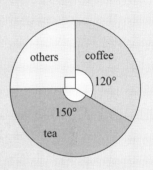

2 This pie chart shows the favourite 'spirits' chosen
by 480 people.
How many people chose:
a vodka   **b** gin   **c** brandy

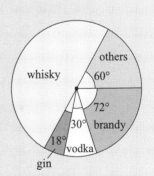

3 10,000 people were surveyed about which continent they
would prefer to buy their car from.
The pie chart shows this information.
Find the angle on the pie chart for:
a Europe   **b** Asia   **c** America

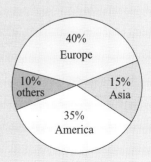

4 The pie charts below show the favourite sports of students from Canning High School and Henton Park School.

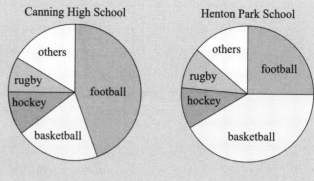

Canning High School

Henton Park School

Explain why you *cannot* say that more students like football in Canning High School than in Henton Park School.

TASK 13.4

M only

1 400 people were asked if they could drive or not. The information is shown in the two-way table.

	drive	not drive	Total
Female	110		170
Male			
Total	290		400

a Copy and complete the table.
b How many males could not drive?

2 When they last recycled something, 600 children were asked if they recycled paper, bottles or cans. The information is shown in the two-way table below.

	paper	bottles	cans	Total
Boys		73	89	
Girls				352
Total	306	131		600

a Copy and complete the two-way table.
b How many girls recycled paper last time they recycled something?

3 Some people were asked if they would rather watch a film on a dvd,
at the cinema or go to the theatre.
The results are shown below:
M = Male, F = Female, d = dvd, c = cinema, t = theatre

M, c	M, c	F, c	F, d	F, c
F, d	F, t	F, d	M, t	M, c
M, c	F, c	M, c	F, t	F, d
F, d	F, d	M, t	M, d	F, c

   a Put these results into a two-way table.
   b What percentage of the males chose the theatre?

4 500 students in the Kingsley High School were asked what they planned
to do after Year 11. The results are shown in the two-way table below.

	stay in 6th. form	go to college	leave education	Total
Year 10			26	
Year 11	120	109	31	
Total	206			500

   a Copy and complete the two-way table.
   b One of these students is picked at random. Write down the
      probability that the student is in Year 10.
   c One of these students is picked at random. Write down the
      probability that the student plans to go to College.

SHAPE 3   15

TASK 15.1

M

1 Find the perimeter of each shape below. All lengths are in cm.

   a

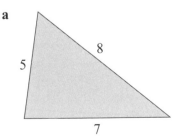

   b

   c

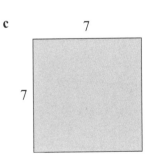

98

2 Draw 3 different rectangles with a perimeter of 14 cm.

3 For each shape below you are given the perimeter. Find the missing value x.
All lengths are in cm.

a

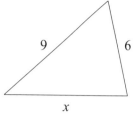

perimeter = 23 cm

b

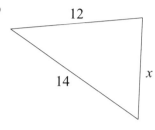

perimeter = 35 cm

c

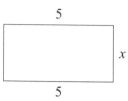

perimeter = 30 cm

4 The perimeter of this square is 24 cm.
Find the missing value x.

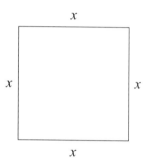

5 The perimeter of these two rectangles is the same. Find the missing value x.

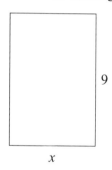

E

1 All lengths are in cm.
 a Find the length of a and b.
 b Find the perimeter of this shape.

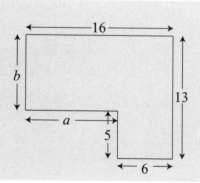

In Questions **2** to **4**, find the perimeter of each shape. All lengths are in cm.

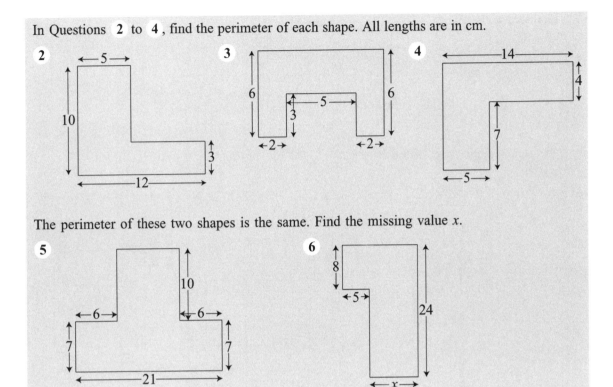

The perimeter of these two shapes is the same. Find the missing value *x*.

TASK 15.2

M

Find the area of each shape below. All lengths are in cm.

1
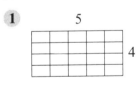

2
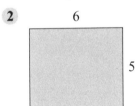

3
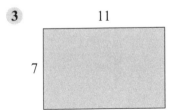

4
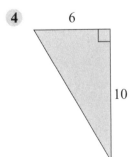

5
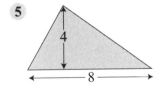

6
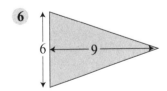

7 Find the value of x.

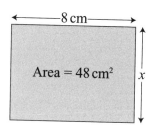

Area = 48 cm²

8 cm

x

Find the area of each shape in Questions **8** to **13** by splitting them into rectangles or triangles.

8

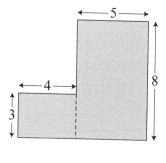

5

4

3

8

9

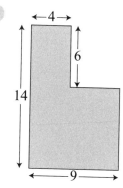

4

6

14

9

10

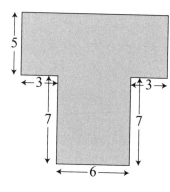

5

3

3

7

7

6

11

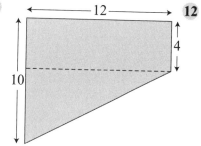

12

4

10

12

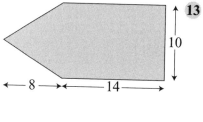

10

8

14

13

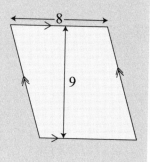

25

7

20

E

Find the area of each shape below. All lengths are in cm.

1

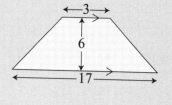

3

6

17

2

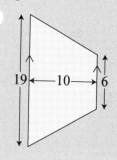

19

10

6

3

8

9

4 The area of this trapezium is 80 cm². What is the value of h?

←3 cm→

h

←7 cm→

5 The area of the parallelogram is equal to the area of the trapezium. Find the value of x.

6 cm

←x cm→

6 cm ←8 cm→ 12 cm

6 Find the shaded area.

←30 m→

20 m

←24 m→

←40 m→

TASK 15.3

M

1 What is the radius of a circle if the diameter is 46 cm?

2 What is the diameter of a circle if the radius is 19 mm?

3 *Use a calculator* to find the circumference of each circle below (give answers to 1 decimal place).

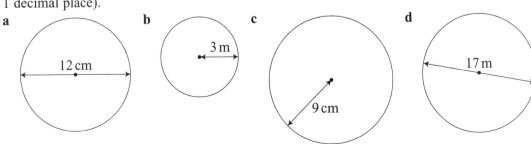

a   12 cm

b   3 m

c   9 cm

d   17 m

4 Which shape has the larger perimeter – the triangle or the circle?

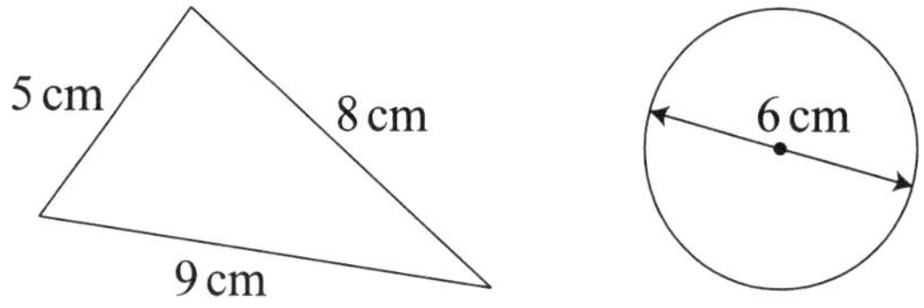

5 cm 8 cm 9 cm 6 cm

5 Which circle has the larger perimeter?

4 cm 7 cm

A B

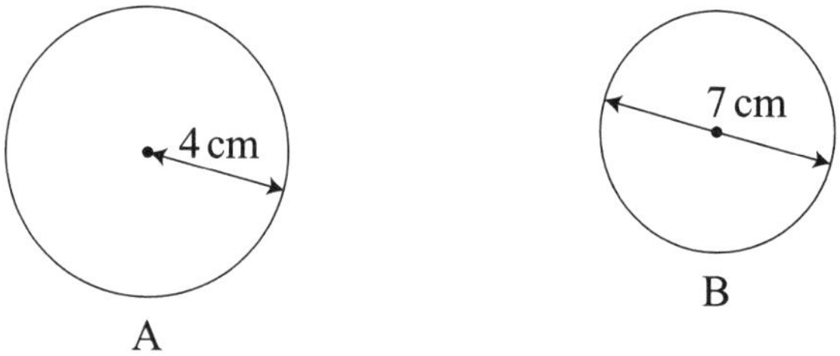

E

Calculate the perimeter of each shape. All arcs are either semi-circles or quarter circles. Give answers correct to 1 decimal place.

1 ← 16 cm →

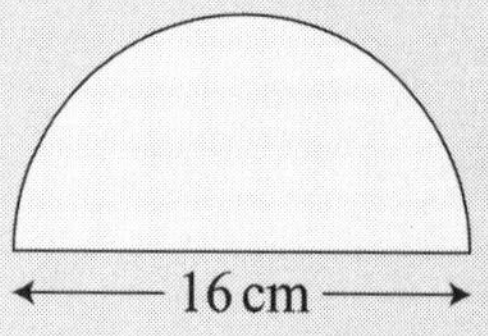

2 31 cm

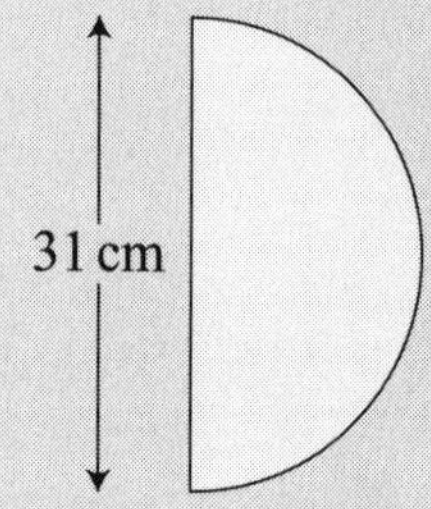

3 5 cm ← 5 cm →

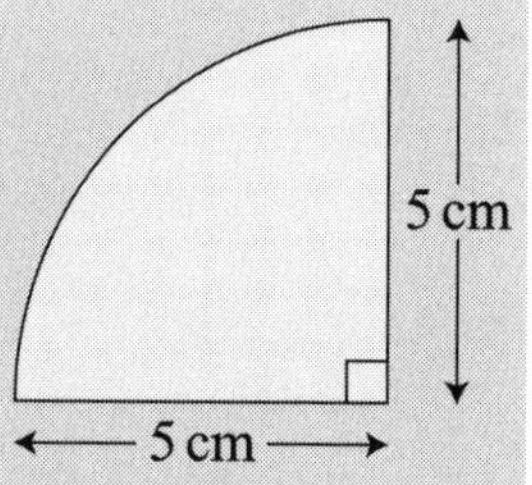

4 ← 12 cm → 4 cm

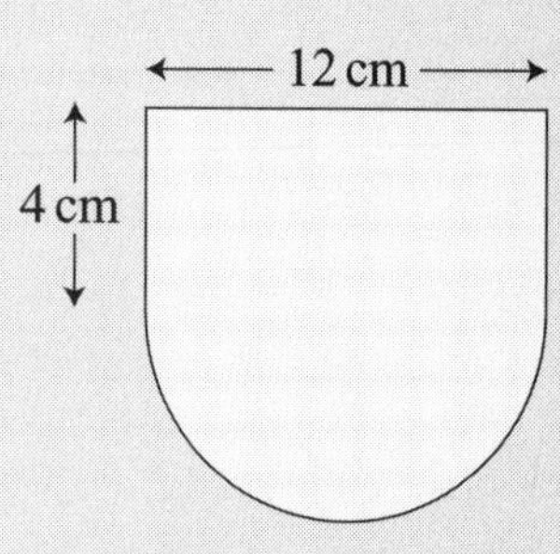

5 ← 100 m → 32 m

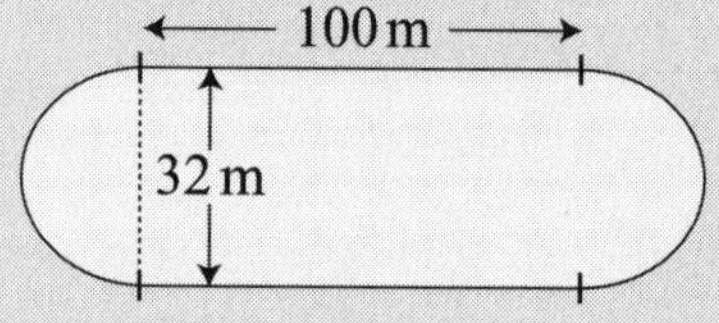

6 ← 3 m → 6 m 3 m

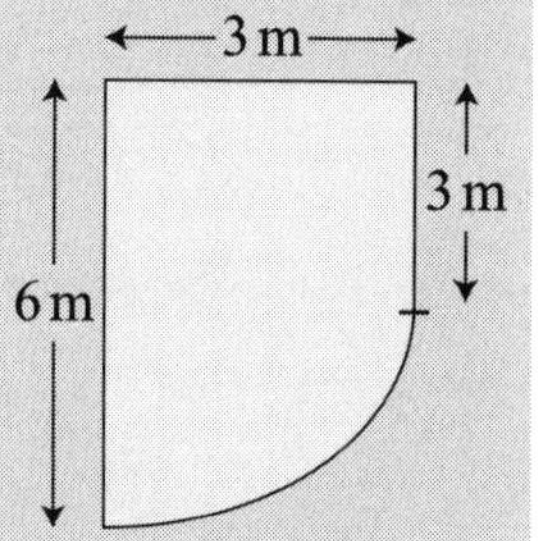

7 A circular log of diameter 30 cm is rolled down a hill. It rolls 48 metres. How many *complete* revolutions did the log make before it stopped?

8 Maisy has a bike with wheels of radius 31·5 cm. She cycles 3 km. How many times do the wheels of her bike go round completely?

TASK 15.4

M

Calculate the area of each circle below, correct to 1 decimal place.

1
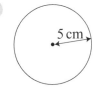
5 cm

2
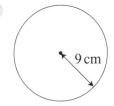
9 cm

3
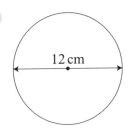
12 cm

4
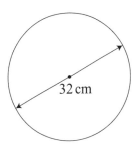
32 cm

5   A circular pond has a radius of 11 m. What is the area of this pond in m²?

6   Which shape has the larger area – the triangle or the circle?

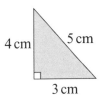
4 cm   5 cm
3 cm

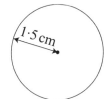
1·5 cm

7   Find the shaded area.

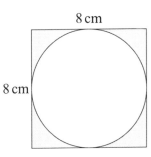
8 cm
8 cm

E

In Questions **1** to **3** find the area of each shape. All arcs are either semi-circles or quarter circles and the units are cm. Give answers correct to 1 decimal place.

1
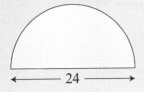
24

2
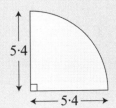
5·4
5·4

3
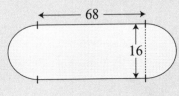
68
16

In Questions **4** to **6** find the shaded area. Lengths are in cm. Give answers correct to 1 decimal place.

4

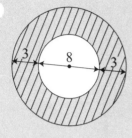

5

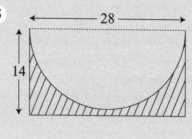

6

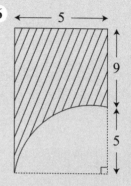

7 A circular pond has a radius of 13 m. A path goes all the way round the circumference of the pond. The path is 1·2 m wide throughout. Find the area of the path.

TASK 15.5

M

1 Copy and complete the table below to find the total surface area of the cuboid.

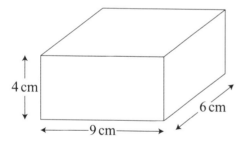

face	area (cm^2)
front	
back	
top	
bottom	
side 1	
side 2	
Total =	

2 Find the volume in cm^3 of the cuboid in Question **1**.

3

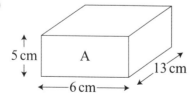

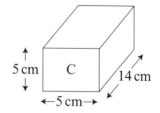

a Which of these 3 cuboids has the largest surface area?

b What is the *difference* between the largest surface area and the smallest surface area?

c Which of the cuboids has the smallest volume?

d What is the *difference* between the largest volume and the smallest volume?

E

1 Which is the greater amount? $7 \cdot 2 \ m^3$ or $7\,090\,000 \ cm^3$

2 True or false? $6 \cdot 3 \ m^2 = 630 \ cm^2$

3 Does $5 \cdot 84 \ m^3 = 58\,400 \ cm^3$ or $5\,840\,000 \ cm^3$?

4 How many *litres* of water will each tank below contain when full?

> **Remember:**
> $1 \ m^3 = 1000$ litres
> $1 \ m^3 =$
> $1\,000\,000 \ cm^3$
> $1 \ m^2 = 10\,000 \ cm^2$

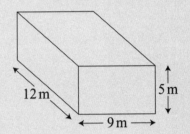

a — 12 m, 9 m, 5 m

b — 3·6 m, 18 m, 4·2 m

5 A rectangular tank has a length of 8 m and a width of 6 m. How high is the tank if it can hold 240 000 litres of water when full?

6 Copy and complete
   a $4 \ m^3 = \boxed{} \ cm^3$ **b** $2 \cdot 9 \ m^3 = \boxed{} \ cm^3$ **c** $8 \ m^2 = \boxed{} \ cm^2$

   d $7 \cdot 48 \ m^2 = \boxed{} \ cm^2$ **e** $6\,000\,000 \ cm^3 = \boxed{} \ m^3$ **f** $6 \ m^3 = \boxed{}$ litres

   g $6\,000\,000 \ cm^2 = \boxed{} \ m^2$ **h** $5 \cdot 16 \ m^3 = \boxed{}$ litres   **i** $38\,000 \ cm^2 = \boxed{} \ m^2$

   j $473\,000 \ cm^2 = \boxed{} \ m^2$ **k** $12 \cdot 64 \ m^3 = \boxed{}$ litres   **l** $0 \cdot 07 \ m^3 = \boxed{} \ cm^3$

TASK 15.6

M

Find the volume of each prism below:

> **Remember:**
> Volume of a prism = area of cross-section × length

1

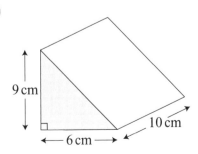

9 cm, 6 cm, 10 cm

2

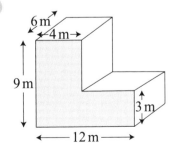

6 m, 4 m, 9 m, 3 m, 12 m

3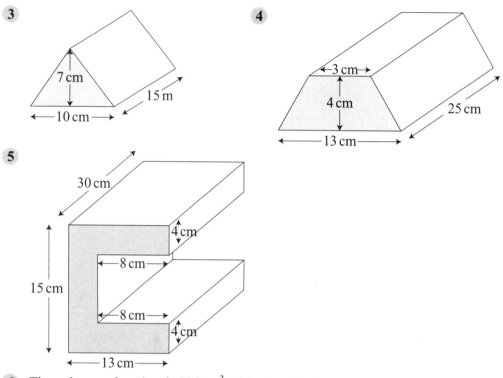

7 cm
15 m
10 cm

4

3 cm
4 cm
25 cm
13 cm

5

30 cm
4 cm
8 cm
15 cm
8 cm
4 cm
13 cm

6 The volume of a prism is 296 cm³. If the length of the prism is 8 cm, what is its cross-sectional area?

E

Find the volume of each cylinder below. *Use a calculator* and give each answer to 1 decimal place.

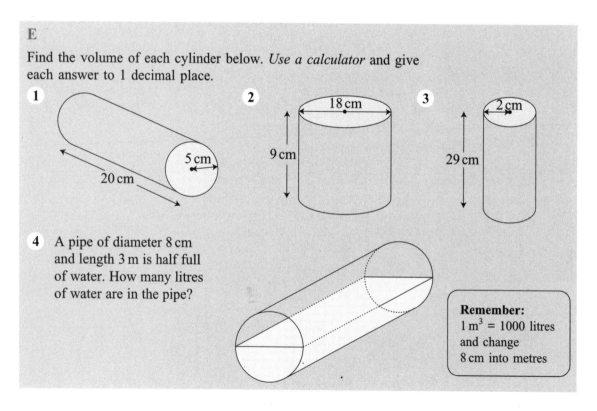

1

5 cm
20 cm

2

18 cm
9 cm

3

2 cm
29 cm

4 A pipe of diameter 8 cm and length 3 m is half full of water. How many litres of water are in the pipe?

Remember:
1 m³ = 1000 litres
and change
8 cm into metres

5 Find the volume of this prism.

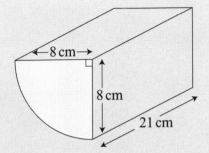

6 A cylindrical bucket has a diameter of
30 cm and a height of 35 cm.
How many full bucket loads of water
are needed to fill up the tank opposite?

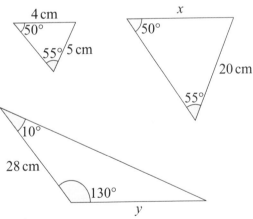

TASK M15.7

M

1 **a** *Explain* why these triangles are similar.
b Find x.

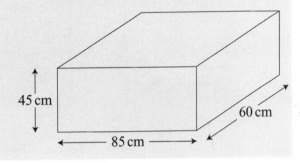

2 Find y.

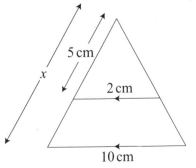

3 Use similar triangles to find x.

4 Use similar triangles to find *y*.

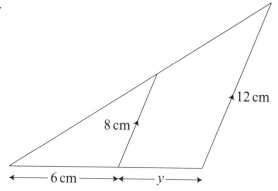

5 Use similar triangles to find *x* in each diagram below.

a

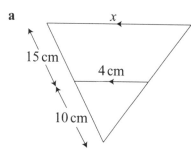

b

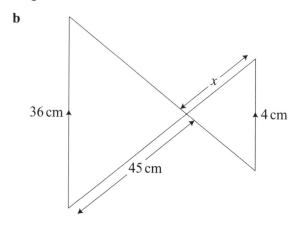

E

1 *a* and *b* are lengths.
   $H = ab^2$ Is this a formula for a length, area or volume?

2 *r* is a length.
   $p = 4\pi r$ Is this a formula for a length, area or volume?

3 Each letter below is a length. For each expression write down if it represents a length, area or volume.

   a $3h$ **b** x^2 **c** $4xy$
   d πabc **e** $3\pi x$ **f** πxy
   g $6\pi r$ **h** $3x^2 y$ **i** $4rh$
   j $5r$ **k** $4xyz$ **l** $7x$
   m $3\pi ab$ **n** $2\pi a^2$ **o** $5y^3$

4 *a*, *b* and *c* are lengths.
   Which of the formulas below represent a volume?

   $6a^3$ πac $7\pi b$ $\pi b^2 c$ $2ab^2$

DATA 3   16

TASK 16.1

M

1 The table below shows the English test results and heights of 16 students.

| Score (%) | 82 | 53 | 80 | 76 | 67 | 46 | 67 | 71 | 61 | 83 | 72 | 48 | 73 | 75 | 59 | 45 |
| Height (cm) | 175 | 182 | 193 | 160 | 168 | 165 | 183 | 197 | 159 | 163 | 175 | 161 | 164 | 188 | 170 | 193 |

a Copy and complete this scatter graph to show the data in the table.

b Describe the correlation in this scatter graph.

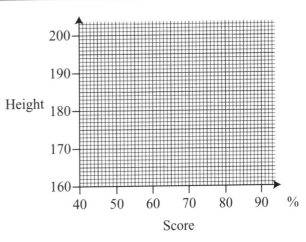

2 Describe the correlation in this scatter graph.

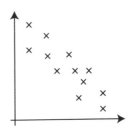

E

1 Write down what X and Y might be to give this scatter graph.

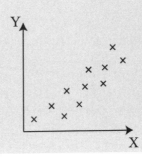

2 The table below shows the heights and neck lengths of 14 people.

height (cm)	177	187	195	162	200	175	192	186	165	200	172	198	181	190
neck length (cm)	6·9	7·5	7·5	5·5	8·5	6·1	6·8	6·8	6	8	5·7	7·7	6·9	7·8

a Copy and complete this scatter graph to show the data in the table.
b Describe the correlation.
c Draw the line of best fit.
d A person is 184 cm tall. Use your line of best fit to find out the person's likely neck length.
e Another person has a neck length of 7·7 cm. How tall is that person likely to be?

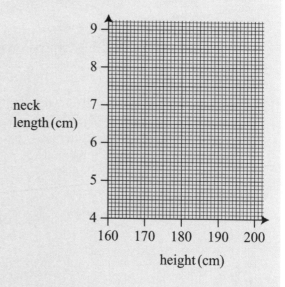

3 This scattergraph shows information about cars. Write down what you think Y might be.

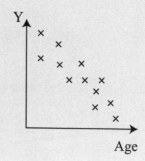

TASK 16.2

M

1 The table below shows the weights of some people.

Weight (kg)	60	61	62	63
Frequency	3	6	5	1

Find **a** the modal weight
       b the median weight

2 The table below shows the number of drinks some children had during one day.

Number of drinks	1	2	3	4	5
Frequency	7	12	8	23	29

Find **a** the modal number of drinks
b the median number of drinks

3 The 2 tables below show the number of GCSE grade Cs obtained by some students.

Number of C grades	1	2	3	4	5
Frequency	20	38	18	27	24

Boys

Number of C grades	1	2	3	4	5
Frequency	26	20	41	39	67

Girls

a Find the median number of C grades for the boys.
b Find the median number of C grades for the girls.
c Which group has the higher median number of C grades?

E

1 The table below shows how many times some people ate meat during one week.

Number of times meat eaten	0 to 1	2 to 5	6 to 8	over 8
Frequency	75	51	104	17

Find **a** the modal interval
b the interval which contains the median

2 The table opposite shows the neck sizes of a group of people.
Find **a** the modal interval
b the interval which contains the median

Neck size (cm)	Frequency
12 to 14	36
$14\frac{1}{2}$ to $15\frac{1}{2}$	81
16 to $16\frac{1}{2}$	75
17 to $17\frac{1}{2}$	29
over $17\frac{1}{2}$	14

3 Some students from nearby schools are asked how often they go each month to a local skateboard park. The information is shown in the tables below.

Chetley Park School	
Park Visits	**Frequency**
0 to 1	27
2 to 5	21
6 to 9	15
10 or more	8

Wetton School	
Park Visits	**Frequency**
0 to 1	19
2 to 5	23
6 to 9	34
10 or more	17

a For each school, find the interval which contains the median.

b From which school do students generally go to the skateboard park more often? Explain why you think this.

TASK 16.3

M

Use a calculator if you need to.

1 Some young people were asked how many different mobile phones they had owned during the last 6 years. The information is shown in the table below.

Number of phones	0	1	2	3	4
Frequency	7	4	12	14	3

a Find the total number of phones.
b Find the mean average number of phones.

2 Some people were asked how many computers they had in total in their houses.
a Find the total number of computers.
b Find the mean average number of computers per house (give your answer to 1 decimal place).

Number of computers	Frequency
0	16
1	26
2	37
3	20
4	5

E

1 Some people were asked how many times they ate out in a restaurant or pub during one month. The information is shown below.

Number of meals (m)	$0 \leqslant m < 2$	$2 \leqslant m < 5$	$5 \leqslant m < 10$	$10 \leqslant m < 20$
Frequency	24	39	16	12

a Estimate the total number of meals.
b Estimate the mean average (give your answer to the nearest whole number).
c *Explain* why your answer is an estimate.

2 The number of goals scored by two hockey teams over the last 15 years is shown in the tables below.

Batton City	
Number of goals (g)	Frequency
$20 \leqslant g < 30$	2
$30 \leqslant g < 40$	3
$40 \leqslant g < 50$	5
$50 \leqslant g < 60$	4
$60 \leqslant g < 70$	1

Chorley Town	
Number of goals (g)	Frequency
$20 \leqslant g < 30$	2
$30 \leqslant g < 40$	6
$40 \leqslant g < 50$	4
$50 \leqslant g < 60$	3
$60 \leqslant g < 70$	0

a Which team has scored the higher mean average number of goals?
b Write down the value of the higher mean average (give your answer to one decimal place).
c What is the *difference* between the mean average number of goals scored by each team?

TASK 16.4

M

1 The hourly rates of pay for 5 workers at a baker's shop are £5·30, £5·30, £6·80, £5·75 and £7·25.

The hourly rates of pay at a butcher's shop for 6 workers are £5·65, £6·75, £8·30, £5·90, £5·90 and £6.

Copy and complete the statements below to compare the pay rates of the 2 shops.

Baker's shop: median = £_____ range = £_____
Butcher's shop: median = £_____ range = £_____

'The median for the baker's shop is (*greater/smaller*) than the median for the butcher's shop. The range for the baker's shop is (*greater/smaller*) than the range for the butcher's shop (i.e. the pay rates for the baker's shop are (*more/less*) spread out).'

2 The number of 'fizzy' drinks drunk each week by some children is shown below:

Class 8C: 2 3 2 5 3 0 1 2 1 3 6 4 3 4
Class 8D: 0 3 1 7 2 0 2 5 6 2 3 1 2

Copy and complete the statements below to compare the number of 'fizzy' drinks drunk by these children in class 8C and class 8D.

Class 8C: mode = _____ range = _____
Class 8D: mode = _____ range = _____

'The mode for class 8C is (*greater/smaller*) than the mode for class 8D and the range of class 8C is (*greater/smaller*) than the range of class 8D (i.e. the number of 'fizzy' drinks drunk in class 8C is (*more/less*) spread out).'

E

1 Sam and Polly record the number of e-mails they receive each day during January. The information is shown below:

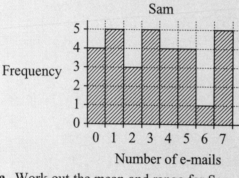
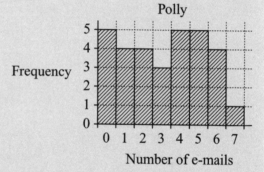

Sam — Number of e-mails

Polly — Number of e-mails

a Work out the mean and range for Sam.
b Work out the mean and range for Polly.
c Write a sentence to compare the number of e-mails received each day by Sam and Polly.

2 Some 8 year-olds and some 18 year-olds are asked how many Christmas presents they had last Christmas.

8 year-olds	
0 to 8	6
9 to 16	31
17 to 24	48
25 to 32	10
33 to 40	3
41 to 48	2

18 year-olds	
0 to 8	34
9 to 16	26
17 to 24	9
25 to 32	5
33 to 40	1
41 to 48	0

a Estimate the mean average for the 8 year-olds.
b Estimate the mean average for the 18 year-olds.
c Compare the number of Christmas presents received by the 8 year-olds and the 18 year-olds.

SHAPE 4   17

TASK 17.1

M

Write down the time shown by each clock below:

1

2

3

4

5

6

7 Write down the measurement indicated by each arrow.

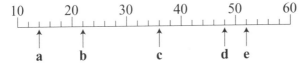

    f Write down the difference between **d** and **b**.
    g Write down the difference between **e** and **a**.

8 Write down the measurement shown by each arrow below.

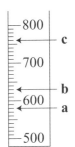
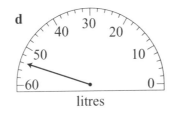
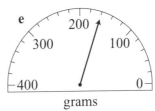

E

1 Write down the measurement indicated by each arrow.

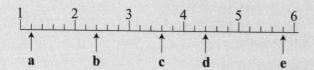

f Write down the difference between **d** and **a**.
g Write down the difference between **e** and **b**.

2 Write down the measurement shown by each arrow below.

a

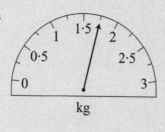

b

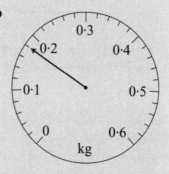

c

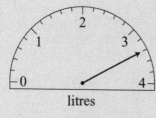

d

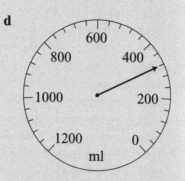

3 Write down the measurement shown by each arrow below.

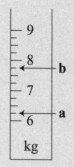

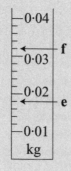

TASK 17.2

M

1 Write each length in cm.
    a 3 m   **b** 1·2 m   **c** 5·8 m   **d** 3·64 m   **e** 0·7 m

2 Write each mass in grams.
    a 4 kg   **b** 6·5 kg   **c** 3·2 kg   **d** 4·718 kg   **e** 0·9 kg

3 Which metric unit would you use to measure:
    a the length of a car   **b** the mass of a car   **c** the width of a pin

4 Sam says that his dad weighs about 80 grams. Is this likely to be a good estimate?

5 Write each length in metres.
    a 600 cm   **b** 450 cm   **c** 5 km   **d** 5·3 km   **e** 7·186 km

6 Write each quantity in ml.
    a 8 litres   **b** 9·5 litres   **c** 4·6 litres   **d** 4·315 litres   **e** 60 cm^3

7 Venkata has a 1 litre bottle of lemonade. If 560 ml of lemonade is used, how much is left in the bottle?

8 Toby is running in a 3 km race. He has covered 900 metres. How much further to the end of the race?

> **Remember:**
> 10 mm = 1 cm
> 100 cm = 1 m
> 1000 m = 1 km
> 1000 g = 1 kg
> 1000 kg = 1 tonne
> 1000 ml = 1 litre
> 1 ml = 1 cm^3

E

1 Barry buys a 2·5 kg bag of potatoes. If he uses up 820 g of potatoes, what weight is left in the bag?

2 Beth walks 3·8 km and Simone walks 937 m. How much further has Beth walked than Simone?

3 Copy and complete the following:
    a 2·6 m = ☐ cm   **b** 3·82 m = ☐ cm   **c** 470 cm = ☐ m

    d 90 mm = ☐ cm   **e** 4 mm = ☐ cm   **f** 1500 m = ☐ km

    g 3·5 kg = ☐ g   **h** 600 g = ☐ kg   **i** 0·28 kg = ☐ g

    j 1·9 tonnes = ☐ kg   **k** 620 ml = ☐ litres   **l** 1937 litres = ☐ ml

    m 8·2 litres = ☐ ml   **n** 3·26 litres = ☐ ml   **o** 43 g = ☐ kg

4 A shop uses 40 g of cheese in one sandwich. How many sandwiches will the shop make if it has 3·2 kg of cheese?

5 Write the following amounts in order of size, starting with the smallest.
    a 8 cm, 0·81 m, 7·4 cm, 83 mm
    b 780 g, 0·7 kg, 738 g, 0·79 kg
    c 5 km, 57 m, 509 m, 0·6 km, 4·7 km
    d 274 ml, 0·28 l, 0·279 l, 275 ml, 2·14 l

TASK 17.3

M

1 For each statement below, write true or false:
a 8:30 p.m. = 20:30
b 4:30 a.m. = 16:30
c 2:15 a.m. = 02:15
d 3:42 a.m. = 03:42
e 10:50 p.m. = 10:50
f 5:17 p.m. = 17:17

2 Sunil watches a 2 hour 15 minute film which starts at 7:50 p.m.
At what time does the film end?

3 Patsy flies to Rome and arrives at 13:35. If the flight lasted for 2 hours
45 minutes, when did the flight begin?

4 Gabby borrows some money and has to pay it back within 5 years.
How many months does she have to pay back the money?

5 Gareth wakes up at the time shown on the clock.
He has to be at work by 9 a.m. How long has he
got before he must be at work?

6 André needs to be at Waterloo station by 5:30 p.m. A train leaves his
home town at 15:48 and takes 1 hour 40 minutes to get to Waterloo
station. Will he arrive at Waterloo station in time?

7 Copy and complete this bus timetable. Each bus takes the same time
between stops.

	Bus 1	Bus 2	Bus 3	Bus 4	Bus 5
Bus Station	07:50	08:35	08:55	09:45	10:25
Cinema	07:59				
Town Hall	08:10				
Cherry Hill	08:22		09:27		
Train Station	08:35			10:30	

E

1 Write each length in inches.
a 5 feet
b 8 feet
c 5 feet 4 inches
d 4 feet 9 inches

2 Write each volume in pints.
a 3 gallons
b 5 gallons
c $3\frac{1}{2}$ gallons
d $2\frac{3}{4}$ gallons

3 Which imperial unit would you use to measure:
a the mass of a man
b the length of a book
c the height of a house

Remember:
12 inches = 1 foot
3 feet = 1 yard
1760 yards = 1 mile
8 pints = 1 gallon
16 ounces = 1 pound
14 pounds = 1 stone
2240 pounds = 1 ton

4   Mary is 4 feet 10 inches tall when she is 11 years old. Over the
    next 5 years she grows 7 inches. How tall is she now?

5   Jade runs 1285 yards. How much further must she run to complete
    1 mile?

6   Copy and complete the following:
    a 2·5 gallons = ☐ pints   **b** 3 stone 2 pounds = ☐ pounds
    c 5 stone 9 pounds = ☐ pounds   **d** 3 miles = ☐ yards
    e 36 pints = ☐ gallons   **f** 98 pounds = ☐ stone
    g 5 tons = ☐ pounds   **h** 7 stone 12 pounds = ☐ pounds
    i $1\frac{1}{2}$ tons = ☐ pounds   **j** 5 feet 10 inches = ☐ inches

TASK 17.4

M

1   Copy and complete:
    a 10 gallons ≈ ☐ litres   **b** 20 kg ≈ ☐ pounds
    c 4 gallons ≈ ☐ litres   **d** 6 inches ≈ ☐ cm
    e 10 miles ≈ ☐ km   **f** $2\frac{1}{2}$ feet ≈ ☐ cm
    g 18 ounces ≈ ☐ g   **h** 27 litres ≈ ☐ gallons
    i 17·5 cm ≈ ☐ inches   **j** $3\frac{1}{2}$ yards ≈ ☐ cm

> **Remember:**
> 1 inch ≈ 2·5 cm
> 1 foot ≈ 30 cm
> 1 yard ≈ 90 cm
> 1 mile ≈ 1·6 km
> 1 ounce ≈ 30 g
> 1 kg ≈ 2·2 pounds
> 1 litre ≈ 1·8 pints
> 1 gallon ≈ 4·5 litres

2   Harry cycles 20 miles. Louise cycles 30 km. Who cycles further?

3   Tom needs 6·5 pounds of flour. If he buys a 2 kg bag of flour and
    a 1 kg bag of flour, will he have enough flour?

4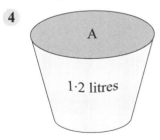
    If each container is
    filled up with water,
    which container will
    hold the most?

5   Which amount is the smaller?
    a 3 gallons or 14 litres?   **b** 8 miles or 12 km?
    c 5 km or 3 miles?   **d** 5 kg or 10 pounds?
    e 8 yards or 700 cm?   **f** 35 litres or 8 gallons?
    g 9 inches or 23 cm?   **h** 4 feet or 1 m?

E

1 The length of a book is 23·4 cm, measured to the nearest 0·1 cm.

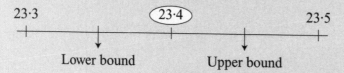

Write down
a the lower bound   **b** the upper bound

2 The width of a room is 3·8 m, measured to the nearest 0·1 m.
Write down
a the lower bound   **b** the upper bound

3 A woman weighs 63 kg, correct to the nearest kg. What is her least possible weight?

4 Copy and complete the table.

A length l is 47·2 cm, to the nearest 0·1 cm, so		$\leqslant l <$	47·25
A mass m is 83 kg, to the nearest kg, so		$\leqslant m <$	
A volume V is 7·3 m³, to the nearest 0·1 m³, so		$\leqslant V <$	
A radius r is 6·87 cm, to the nearest 0·01 cm, so		$\leqslant r <$	
An area A is 470 m², to the nearest 10 m², so		$\leqslant A <$	

5 The base and height of a triangle are measured to the nearest 0·1 cm.
a Write down the upper bound for the base 3·4 cm.
b Write down the lower bound for the height 4·8 cm.
c The area of the triangle is $\frac{1}{2}$ (base × height).
Use a calculator to find the *greatest* possible value of the area of the triangle.

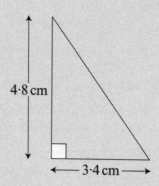

6 The length, width and height of the cuboid are measured to the nearest cm.

volume = length × width × height

Use a calculator to find the *lowest* possible value of the volume of the cuboid.

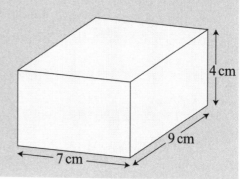

TASK 17.5

M

Use △D/S|T to help you work out the Questions below:

1 Find the speed for each distance and time shown below.
   a distance = 60 miles, time = 3 hours
   b distance = 325 km, time = 5 hours

2 Find the distance for each speed and time shown below.
   a speed = 45 mph, time = 2 hours
   b speed = 58 mph, time = $\frac{1}{2}$ hour

3 Find the time taken for each distance and speed shown below.
   a distance = 280 km, speed = 70 km/hr
   b distance = 50 km, speed = 20 km/hr

4 Copy and complete this table.

Distance (km)	Time (hours)	Speed (km/hr)
324	9	
	4	51
	1·5	60
150		25
245		35
40	0·5	

5 Jack cycles 3 km in 15 minutes. What was his average speed in km/hr?

6 Brenda drives from Nottingham to Leeds at an average speed of 84 km/hr. The journey takes 1 hour 30 minutes. How far is it from Nottingham to Leeds?

7 A train travels 47 km in 20 minutes. What is the speed of the train in km/hr?

8 Ellen drives 24 km from her home to work. She travels at an average speed of 32 km/hr. If she leaves home at 8·05 a.m., when will she arrive at work?

E

Use △M/D|V to help you work out the Questions below:

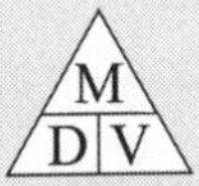

1 A solid weighs 450 g and has a volume of 50 cm^3. Find the density of this solid.

2 A liquid has a density of 2 g/cm^3. How much does the liquid weigh if its volume is 240 cm^3?

3 A metal bar has a density of 12 g/cm^3 and a mass of 360 g.
Find the volume of the metal bar.

4 Copy and complete this table.

Density (g/cm^3)	Mass (g)	Volume (cm^3)
7		90
	240	60
8	152	
	42	0·5
13	585	
1·5		140

5 Gold has a density of 19·3 g/cm^3. A gold ring has a volume of 1·1 cm^3.
Find the mass of the gold ring.

6 A brass handle has a volume of 17 cm^3 and a mass of 139·4 g.
Find the density of the brass.

7 Which has a greater volume −102·6 g of lead with density 11·4 g/cm^3 or 78·85 g of steel with density 8·3 g/cm^3? Write down by how much.

8 The density of this metal bar is 7·4 g/cm^3.
Find the mass of this metal bar.
Give your answer in kg.
(Note the length is given in metres)

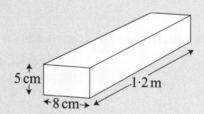

9 A curtain material costs £38 per metre. How much will 4·5 m cost?

10 Each year a farmer makes a profit of 90p per m^2 in this triangular field. How much profit does he make in total? Give your answer in pounds.

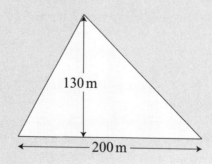

ALGEBRA 4 18

TASK 18.1

M

Copy and complete each statement below:

1 If $a = b + 4$ then $a \boxed{} 4 = b$

2 If $y = x + 6$ then $y \boxed{} 6 = x$

3 If $x = 4y$ then $\dfrac{x}{\boxed{}} = y$

4 If $a = \dfrac{b}{8}$ then $\boxed{} a = b$

5 $a = b - 10$ Make b the subject of the formula.

6 $n = 5m$ Make m the subject of the formula.

7 Make n the subject of each formula given below:
   a $m = n + 9$ **b** $m = 4n$ **c** $m = \dfrac{n}{3}$ **d** $m = n - 10$

8 Write down the pairs of equations which belong to each other.

$y = 8x$ $y = \dfrac{x}{8}$

$8y = x$ $\dfrac{y}{8} = x$

9 Write down which working out below is correct.
   a $m = 4n + 8$
      $m + 8 = 4n$
      $\dfrac{m + 8}{4} = n$

   b $y = 2x - 6$
      $y + 6 = 2x$
      $\dfrac{y + 6}{2} = x$

10 Make n the subject of each formula given below:
   a $m = 3n + 5$ **b** $m = 7n - 1$ **c** $m = \dfrac{n}{4} - 6$

E

1 Which statements below are true or false?
   a $m = np + v$ so $m - v = np$
   b $y = mx + c$ so $y + c = mx$
   c $p = qs - r$ so $p + r = qs$
   d $mx = y + c$ so $x = \dfrac{y + c}{m}$

2 Make n the subject of each formula given below:
   a $m = cn - f$ **b** $x = gn + h$ **c** $an - 2m = y$

3 Copy and fill each box below:

a $a(x + b) = y$

$ax + \boxed{} = y$

$ax + \boxed{} - \boxed{} = y - \boxed{}$

$ax = y - \boxed{}$

$x = \dfrac{y - \boxed{}}{a}$

b $p(t - 2) = 3q$

$pt - \boxed{} = 3q$

$pt - \boxed{} + \boxed{} = 3q + \boxed{}$

$pt = 3q + \boxed{}$

$t = \dfrac{3q + \boxed{}}{\boxed{}}$

4 Make n the subject of each formula given below:

    a $m(n + p) = v$ **b** $x(n + f) = y$ **c** $h(n - 3) = x$

5 $\dfrac{an - b}{3} = c$ Make n the subject of the formula.

6 $\dfrac{mx + c}{a} = b$ Make x the subject of the formula.

7 $\dfrac{y = 3(b + c)}{m}$ Make b the subject of the formula.

TASK 18.2

M

1 Copy and fill each box below with $<$ or $>$.

    a $15 \boxed{} 19$ **b** $2{\cdot}4 \boxed{} 1{\cdot}4$ **c** $302 \boxed{} 299$ **d** $-3 \boxed{} -4$

2 Answer true or false:

    a $3{\cdot}09 > 3{\cdot}1$ **b** $-8 < -4$ **c** $3\frac{1}{4} > 3{\cdot}5$ **d** $6{\cdot}81 > 6{\cdot}59$

3 If $n \leqslant 4{\cdot}5$, which of the values for n below would be allowed?

$\boxed{4{\cdot}2}$ $\boxed{4\frac{1}{4}}$ $\boxed{4{\cdot}75}$ $\boxed{4{\cdot}06}$ $\boxed{4\frac{1}{2}}$ $\boxed{4{\cdot}914}$

4 shows $x \geqslant 3$  shows $x < 2$

Write down the inequalities shown below:

a    **b**   **c**
6   −3   −1

d    **e**    **f**
2   6   −2   3   −4   0

5 Draw a number line to show the following inequalities.

    a $x \geqslant 1$ **b** $x < -6$ **c** $4 \leqslant x \leqslant 9$

    d $-2 < x < 0$ **e** $-3 \leqslant x < 2$ **f** $-5 < x \leqslant -1$

E

Solve the inequalities below:

1 $x + 6 > 12$

2 $x + 3 < -2$

3 $x - 4 \leqslant 7$

4 $x - 6 < 0$

5 $4x \geqslant 12$

6 $\frac{x}{2} > 9$

7 $3x + 2 > 17$

8 $4x - 8 \leqslant 12$

9 $2(x + 3) < 18$

10 $6(x - 2) \geqslant 24$

11 $6x - 4 > 3x + 17$

12 $\frac{x}{4} - 3 \leqslant 3$

13 Write down the largest *integer* x for which $2x < 7$.

14 Write down the largest *integer* x for which $5x < 12$.

15 Write down all the *integer values* (*whole numbers*) of x which satisfy each inequality below.

a $4 \leqslant x \leqslant 7$

b $0 < x \leqslant 5$

c $-2 < x < 0$

d $-3 \leqslant x \leqslant 3$

e $-4 \leqslant x < -1$

f $-6 < x < 1$

TASK 18.3

M

1 Work out and write each answer as a number in index form.

a $5^3 \times 5^4$

b $6^4 \div 6^2$

c $3^8 \div 3^3$

d $9^4 \times 9^2$

e $2^7 \times 2$

f $4^9 \div 4$

g $2^3 \times 2^4 \times 2^2$

h $5^3 \times 5 \times 5^3$

i $5^6 \times 5^2 \div 5^4$

Remember:
$a^m \times a^n = a^{m+n}$
$a^m \div a^n = a^{m-n}$

2 Copy and complete

a $2^6 \times 2 = \boxed{}$

b $3^4 \times \boxed{} = 3^9$

c $\boxed{} \times 6^3 = 6^7$

d $5^7 \div \boxed{} = 5^2$

e $8^{12} \div \boxed{} = 8^{11}$

f $\boxed{} \div 4^6 = 4^2$

3 Answer true or false for each statement below.

a $2^4 \times 2 = 2^4$

b $4^2 \times 4^4 = 4^8$

c $7^8 \div 7^2 = 7^6$

4 Work out and write each answer as a number in index form.

a $\frac{3^6 \times 3^4}{3^7}$

b $\frac{5^3 \times 5^2 \times 5^2}{5^5}$

c $\frac{9^7}{9^3 \times 9}$

E

1 Work out and write each answer as a number in index form.

a $(4^2)^3$

b $(2^3)^3$

c $(7^4)^2$

d $(5^2)^4 \times 5^3$

e $(6^2) \times (6^2)^2$

f $\frac{(3^2)^5}{3^6}$

g $4^3 \times (4^3)^4$

h $\frac{(2^2)^6}{(2^3)^3}$

i $\frac{7^4 \times (7^3)^2}{7^5}$

Remember:
$(a^m)^n = a^{mn}$
$a^0 = 1$

2 What is the value of 8^0?

3 Simplify the expressions below.

   a $x^4 \times x^3$ **b** $y^7 \times y^2$ **c** $a^6 \div a^2$

   d $\dfrac{m^7}{m^3}$ **e** $(x^2)^4$ **f** x^0

   g $(y^5)^3$ **h** $(a^0)^3$ **i** $(x^3)^2 \div x^2$

4 Answer true or false for each statement below.

   a $(x^4)^5 = x^9$ **b** $y^4 \times y^2 = y^8$ **c** $x^3 \times x = x^3$

   d $\dfrac{n^6}{n} = n^5$ **e** $\dfrac{(x^3)^3}{(x^2)^3} = x^3$ **f** $\dfrac{(a^2)^4}{a} = a^6$

5 Which rectangle has the larger area?

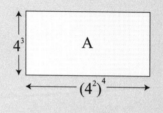
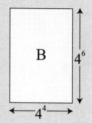

6 Simplify the expressions below.

   a $\dfrac{n^4 \times n^2}{n^5}$ **b** $\dfrac{(x^2)^2 \times x^5}{x^6}$ **c** $\dfrac{a \times (a^3)^3}{(a^3)^2}$

   d $\dfrac{(x^2)^6 \times x^2}{(x^7)^2}$ **e** $\dfrac{m^9}{m^2 \times m^5}$ **f** $\dfrac{n^{10}}{(n^3)^2 \times n^2}$

   g $\dfrac{(x^3)^4 \times (x^2)^5}{(x^3)^6}$ **h** $\dfrac{m^{19}}{(m^2)^4 \times (m^5)^2}$ **i** $\dfrac{(x^3)^3 \times (x^2)^5}{(x^6)^2 \times (x^2)^2}$

7 Answer true or false for each statement below.

   a $3x \times 3x = 9x^2$ **b** $5x^2 \times 4x^3 = 20x^6$

   c $(3a^2)^2 = 9a^4$ **d** $\dfrac{15x^7}{3x^4} = 5x^3$

TASK 18.4

M

1 Write the numbers below in standard form.

   a 3000   **b** 70 000   **c** 340   **d** 89 000

   e 486 000   **f** 598   **g** 9 million   **h** 76 million

Remember:
a standard form number will have the form $A \times 10^n$ where $1 \leqslant A < 10$

2 Remember that $570 = 5 \cdot 7 \times 10^2$ but $0 \cdot 057 = 5 \cdot 7 \times 10^{-2}$. Write the number below in standard form.

   a 0·004   **b** 0·0007   **c** 0·9   **d** 0·0018

   e 0·528   **f** 0·000019   **g** 0·0034   **h** 0·00000817

3 Write each number below as an ordinary number.

a 6×10^4 b 3×10^2 c 3×10^{-2} d 5.6×10^4

e 2.4×10^5 f 8.6×10^{-3} g 4.16×10^3 h 7.68×10^{-1}

4 $3700 = 37 \times 10^2$. *Explain* why this number is not written in standard form.

5 $28\,000 = 28 \times 10^3$. This number is not written in standard form. Write it correctly in standard form.

6 Write the numbers below in standard form.

a 0.0007 b $53\,000$ c 0.096 d 0.487

e $49\,000\,000$ f $576\,000$ g 0.00074 h 82.4

i 0.1 j 0.000000864 k $6\,180\,000$ l $42\,000\,000$

E

1 *Use a calculator* to work out the following and write each answer in standard form.

a $(7 \times 10^8) \times (4 \times 10^9)$

b $(6.2 \times 10^5) \times (3 \times 10^{34})$

c $(4 \times 10^{-8}) \times (6 \times 10^{37})$

d $(3.6 \times 10^{14}) \div (3 \times 10^{-14})$

e $(7.6 \times 10^{-29}) \div (2 \times 10^{-11})$

f $(5.2 \times 10^{37}) + (6.1 \times 10^{36})$

2 The population of the UK is (5.97×10^7) people. The population of the USA is (2.41×10^8) people. What is the combined population of UK and USA? (give your answer in standard form)

3 The mass of an atom is 3.74×10^{-26} grams. What is the total mass of 2 million atoms?

4 Work out the following, leaving each answer in standard form correct to 3 significant figures.

a $\dfrac{(5.6 \times 10^{21}) \times (2.7 \times 10^{28})}{5 \times 10^{13}}$

b $\dfrac{(7.4 \times 10^{-13}) \times (3.94 \times 10^{-26})}{4.2 \times 10^{18}}$

c $\dfrac{(3.8 \times 10^{23}) - (9.7 \times 10^{22})}{1.8 \times 10^{-17}}$

d $\dfrac{(4.89 \times 10^{16})^2}{2.14 \times 10^9}$

e $\dfrac{(4.83 \times 10^{14}) + (3.16 \times 10^{15})}{2.82 \times 10^{-12}}$

f $\dfrac{5.28 \times 10^{31}}{(4.9 \times 10^{-10}) + (2.7 \times 10^{-9})}$

5 *Do not use a calculator.*
Find the area of this rectangle, leaving your answer in standard form.

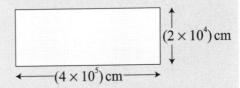

$(2 \times 10^4)\,\text{cm}$

$(4 \times 10^5)\,\text{cm}$

6 *Do not use a calculator.* Work out the following, leaving each answer in standard form.

a $(2 \times 10^8) \times (2.5 \times 10^7)$

b $(1.5 \times 10^6) \times (4 \times 10^3)$

c $(3.5 \times 10^9) \times (2 \times 10^{-4})$

d $(1.7 \times 10^{-18}) \times (4 \times 10^{-8})$

e $(4 \times 10^{12}) \times (3 \times 10^7)$

f $(9 \times 10^{17}) \times (4 \times 10^{28})$

g $(8 \times 10^{21}) \div (4 \times 10^6)$

h $(7 \times 10^{19}) \div (2 \times 10^7)$

i $\dfrac{9 \times 10^{32}}{4\cdot5 \times 10^{-5}}$

j $(4 \times 10^5)^2$

k $(8\cdot7 \times 10^{12}) \div (3 \times 10^{-16})$

l $\dfrac{3 \times 10^{48}}{6 \times 10^{13}}$

7 *Do not use a calculator.* Calli has £(4×10^5) and Carl has £(3×10^4). They put their money together. Write down the total amount of money they have, giving your answer in standard form.

8 In a TV popstar show final, the number of votes for each contestant is shown below:

Gary Tallow $(9\cdot6 \times 10^5)$ votes
Nina X $(1\cdot3 \times 10^6)$ votes
Rosa Williams $(1\cdot85 \times 10^6)$ votes

How many people voted in total? *Do not use a calculator* and give your answer in standard form.

SHAPE 5   19

TASK 19.1

M

1 Measure these lines to the nearest tenth of a centimeter.

2 Which shape below has the larger perimeter and by how much?

a

b
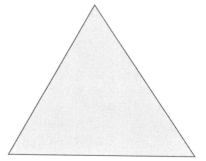

3 Which shape below has the smaller perimeter and by how much?

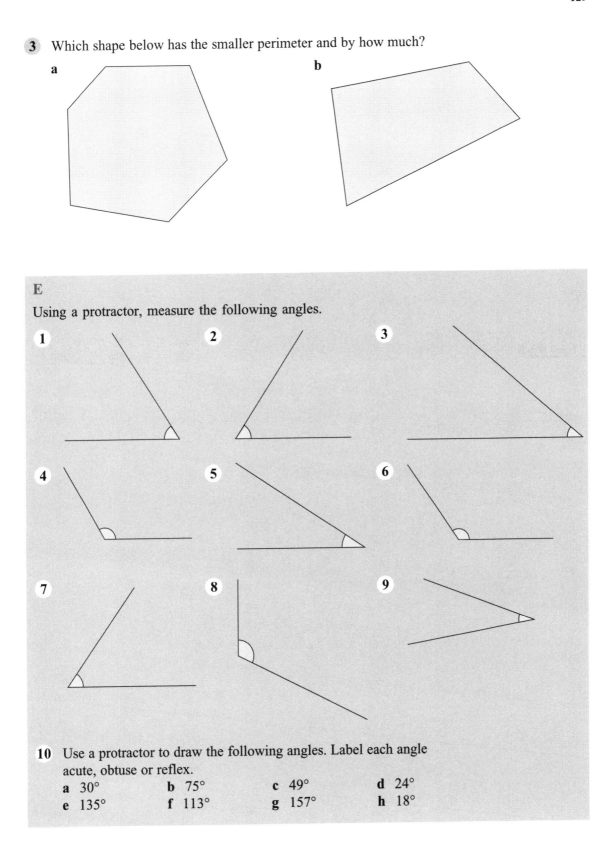

a

b

E

Using a protractor, measure the following angles.

1

2

3

4

5

6

7

8

9

10 Use a protractor to draw the following angles. Label each angle acute, obtuse or reflex.

 a 30°   **b** 75°   **c** 49°   **d** 24°

 e 135°   **f** 113°   **g** 157°   **h** 18°

TASK 19.2

M

1 Use a ruler and protractor to draw:

a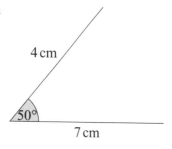

b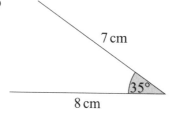

2 **a** Draw accurately the triangle.

b Measure the length of the side marked *x*.

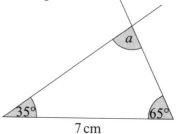

3 **a** Use a ruler and protractor to draw the triangle.

b Measure and write down angle *a*.

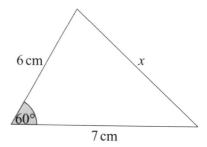

In Questions **4** to **6**, construct the triangles and measure the lengths of the sides marked *x*.

4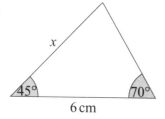

5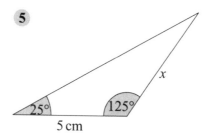

6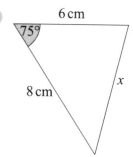

E

In Questions 1 to 3 , use a ruler and compasses only to draw each triangle. Use a protractor to measure each angle *x*.

1
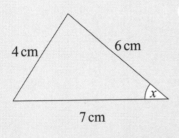

2
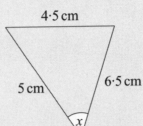

3
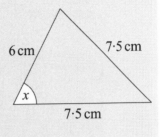

4 Draw accurately an isosceles triangle with two sides equal to 5·5 cm and one side equal to 7 cm. Two of the angles should be the same. Measure one of these angles.

5 Draw a triangle ABC, where AB = 5·2 cm, BC = 7·1 cm and AC = 6·3 cm. Measure ∠ABC.

6 Draw accurately the diagrams below:

a
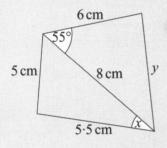

Measure angle *x* and side *y*.

b
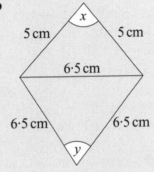

Measure angle *x* and angle *y*.

TASK 19.3

M

1 Draw ∠ABC = 70°.
Construct the bisector of the angle.
Use a protractor to check that
each half of the angle now
measures 35°.

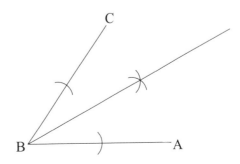

2 Draw any angle and construct the bisector of this angle.

3 Draw a horizontal line AB of length 7 cm. Construct the perpendicular bisector of AB. Check that each half of the line measures 3·5 cm exactly.

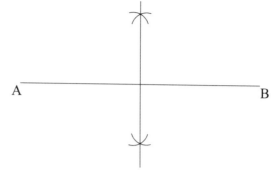

4 Draw any vertical line. Construct the perpendicular bisector of the line.

5 **a** Draw PQ and QR at right angles to each other as shown.
   b Construct the perpendicular bisector of QR.
   c Construct the perpendicular bisector of PQ.
   d The two perpendicular bisectors meet at a point (label this as S). Measure QS.

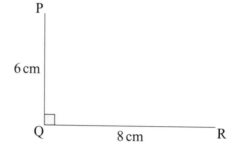

6 **a** Draw ∠ABC = 108° by using a protractor.
   b Construct the bisector of this angle.
   c Construct the bisector of one of the new angles.
   d Check with a protractor that you have now drawn an angle of 27°.

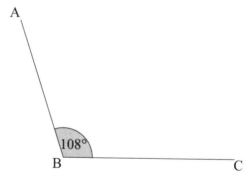

E

1 Construct an equilateral triangle with each side equal to 7 cm.

2 Construct an angle of 60°.

3 **a** Draw a line 8 cm long and mark the point A as shown.

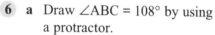

5 cm   A   3 cm

   b Construct an angle of 90° at A.

4 **a** Draw a line 10 cm long and mark the point B on the line as shown.

4 cm   B   6 cm

b Construct an angle of 45° at B.

5 Construct a right-angled triangle ABC, where ∠ABC = 90°, BC = 6 cm and ∠ACB = 60°. Measure the length of AB.

6 Construct this triangle with ruler and compasses only. Measure x.

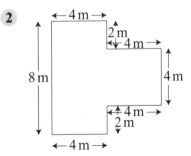

45°   8 cm   60° x

TASK 19.4

M

Draw an accurate scale drawing of each shape below using the scale shown.

1

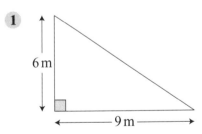

6 m
9 m

Scale: 1 cm for every 3 m

2

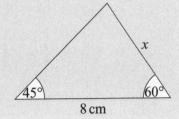

←4 m→
2 m
←4 m→
8 m   4 m
←4 m→
2 m
←4 m→

Scale: 1 cm for every 2 m

3 Make a scale drawing of the front of this house using a scale of 1 cm for every 2 m.

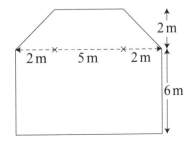

2 m   5 m   2 m   2 m

6 m

4

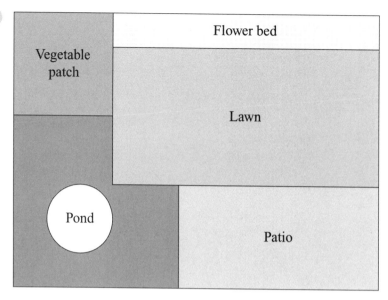

This is a plan of Rosemary's garden. It has been drawn to a scale
of 1 cm for every 3 m.
 a What is the length and width of the lawn? **b** How wide is the patio?
 c What is the diameter of the pond? **d** What is the area of the vegetable patch?

5 **a** How many km is Henton from Catford?
 b How far is Catford from Rigby?
 c How far is Henton from Rigby?

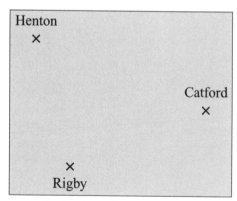

Scale: 1 cm for every 10 km.

E

1 The model of a statue is made using a scale of 1 : 40. If the statue
is 3·2 m tall, how tall is the model (give your answer in cm)?

2 A park is 5 cm long on a map whose scale is 1 : 40 000. Find the
actual length (in km) of the park.

3 Copy and complete the table below.

Map length	Scale	Real length
7 cm	1 : 60	m
5 cm	1 : 2000	m
8 cm	1 : 50 000	km
cm	1 : 100 000	3 km
cm	1 : 4000	320 m
cm	1 : 5 000 000	125 km

4 The distance between two towns is 25 km. How far apart will they be on a map of scale 1 : 500 000?

5 A plan of a house is made using a scale of 1 : 30. The width of the house on the plan is 40 cm. What is the real width of the house? (give your answer in metres)

6 Measure then write down the actual distances (in km) between:
  a Hatton and Bowton
  b Hatton and Tatley
  c Bowton and Tatley

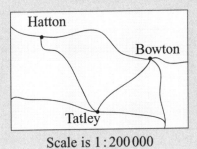

Scale is 1 : 200 000

TASK 19.5

M

You will need a ruler and a pair of compasses.

1 Draw the locus of all points which are less than or equal to 3 cm from a point A.

2 Draw the locus of all points which are exactly 4 cm from a point B.

3 Draw the locus of all points which are exactly 4 cm from the line PQ.

P —————————————— Q
5 cm

4 A triangular garden has a tree at the corner B. The whole garden is made into a lawn except for anywhere less than or equal to 6 m from the tree. Using a scale of 1 cm for 3 m, draw the garden and shade in the lawn.

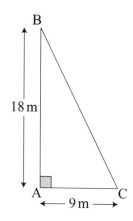

5 A square garden has a fence around its perimeter. A dog inside the garden is attached by a rope to a peg P as shown. The rope is 30 m long. Using a scale of 1 cm for 10 m, copy the diagram then shade the area that the dog can roam in.

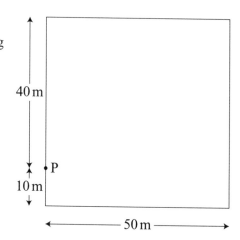

6 Draw the square opposite. Draw the locus of all the points *outside* the square which are 3 cm from the edge of the square.

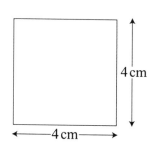

E

You will need a ruler and a pair of compasses.
1 Construct the locus of points which are the same distance from the lines AB and BC (the bisector of angle B).

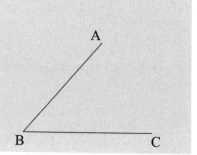

2 A soldier walks across a courtyard from B so that he is always the same distance from AB and BC. Using a scale of 1 cm for 20 m, draw the courtyard and construct the path taken by the soldier.

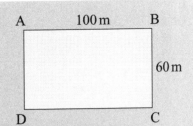

3 Construct the locus of points which are equidistant (the same distance) from M and N.

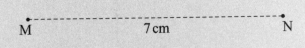

4 Draw this square.
Show the locus of points *inside the square* which are nearer to Q than to S.

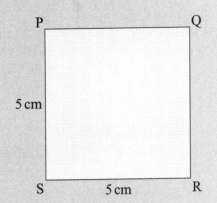

5 Draw A and B 7 cm apart.

A•   •B

A radar at A has a range of 150 km and a radar at B has a range of 90 km.
Using a scale of 1 cm for every 30 km, show the area which can be covered by both radars at the same time.

6 Draw one copy of triangle ABC and show on it:
a the perpendicular bisector of QR.
b the bisector of ∠PRQ.
c the locus of points nearer to PR than to QR *and* nearer to R than to Q.

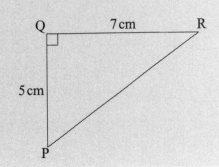

SHAPE 6   20

TASK 20.1

M

1 Draw an accurate net for this cuboid.

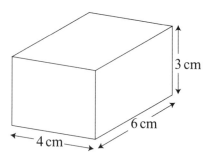

2 This net will fold to make a cube. Copy the net and put a cross X in the square which will be opposite the ● when the cube is made.

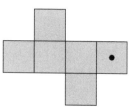

3 This net makes a cuboid. What is the volume of the cuboid?

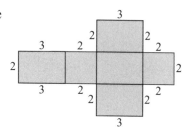

> **Remember:**
> volume of a
> cuboid = length ×
> width × height

4 The two nets below will fold to make cuboids.
Each small square is 1 cm long.
Which cuboid has the greater volume and by how much?

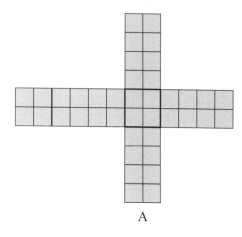

A

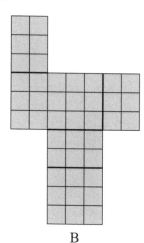

B

E

1 This is a tetrahedron (a triangular pyramid)

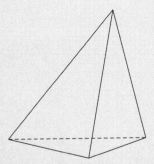

Which of these nets will make a tetrahedron?

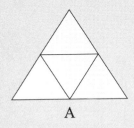

A

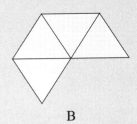

B

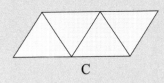

C

2 *Sketch* a net for this triangular prism.

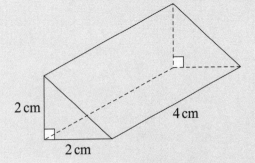

2 cm

2 cm

4 cm

3 *Sketch* a net for this solid (called an octahedron).

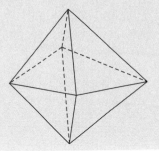

4 **a** Draw a circle with radius 4 cm.
   b Keep the compasses set at 4 cm.
   Place the compass point on the
   circumference of the circle and
   draw an arc across the
   circumference as shown (A).

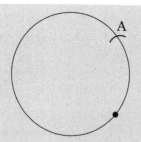

   c Place the compass point on A and draw an arc
   across the circumference. Repeat the
   process right around the circumference
   as shown.

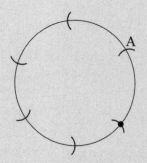

   d Join the points as shown to make
   a hexagon.

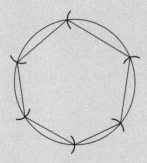

   e Use *compasses* and a *ruler* to
   complete this net for a
   hexagonal-based pyramid.

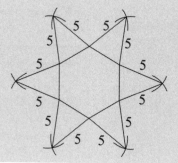

TASK 20.2

M

You will need isometric dot paper.

1. Make a copy of each object below. For each drawing state the number of 'multilink' cubes needed to make the object.

a

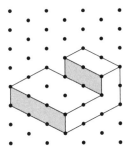

b

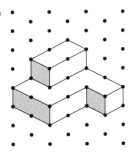

2. Draw a cuboid with a volume of 12 cm³.

3. How many more cubes are needed to make this shape into a cuboid?

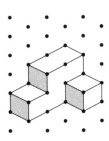

4. **a** Draw a cuboid with length 8 cm, width 3 cm and height 1 cm.
   b Draw a *different* cuboid with the same volume.

5. Draw this object from a *different view*.

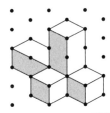

E

1. Draw and label the plan and a side elevation for:
   a a cuboid   **b** a cone

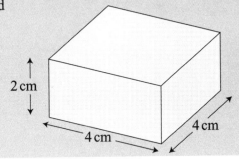

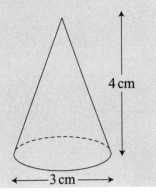

2 You are given the plan and two elevations of an object. Draw each object (on isometric paper if you wish to).

a
front elevation

plan view

side elevation

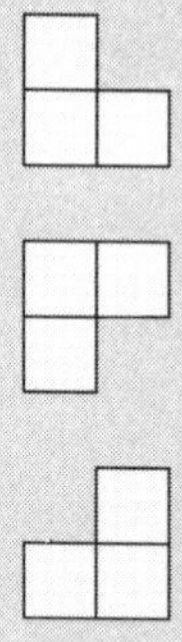

b
front elevation

plan view

side elevation

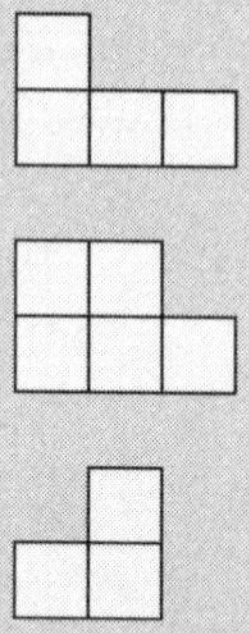

c
front elevation

plan view

side elevation

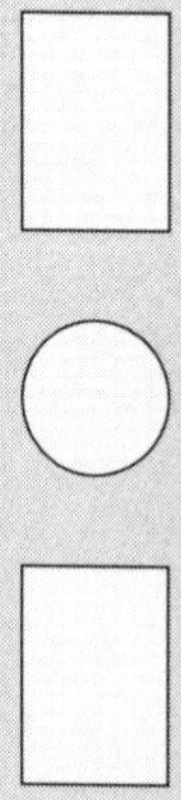

d
front elevation

plan view

side elevation

3 Draw a front elevation, plan view and side elevation of each solid below:

a

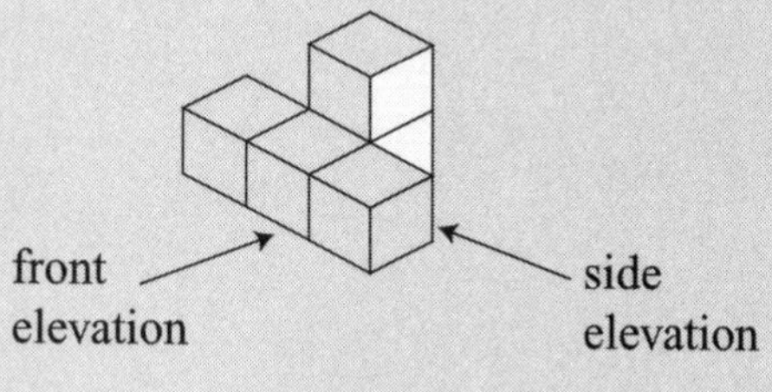

front elevation

side elevation

b

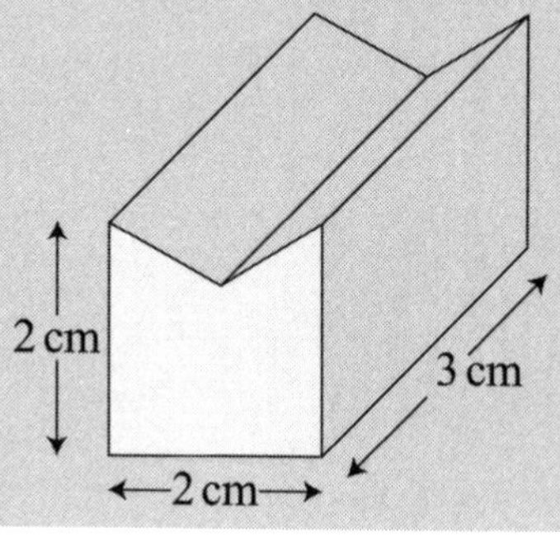

2 cm

3 cm

←2 cm→

TASK 20.3

M

1 4 rabbits escape from their run and race off in the directions shown.
On what bearing does each rabbit race?

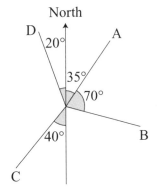

Remember:
a bearing is measured clockwise from the North

2 The point at the centre is called M.
Find the bearing of:
a P *from M*
b S *from M*
c R *from M*
d T *from M*
e Q *from M*

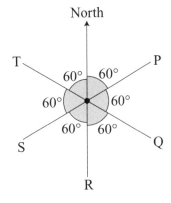

3 Write down the bearing of:
a Barnwoth *from Hoston*
b Rigby *from Hoston*
c Rigby *from Barnworth*
d Hoston *from Barnworth*
e Hoston *from Rigby*

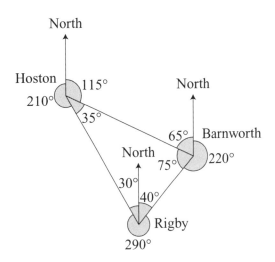

E

1 Use a protractor to measure the bearing of:
   a Harwich *from Melton*
   b Melton *from Harwich*

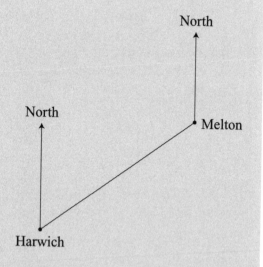

2 Use a protractor to measure the bearing of:
   a Elton *from Saxley*
   b Elton *from Baghill*
   c Saxley *from Baghill*
   d Baghill *from Elton*
   e Saxley *from Elton*
   f Baghill *from Saxley*

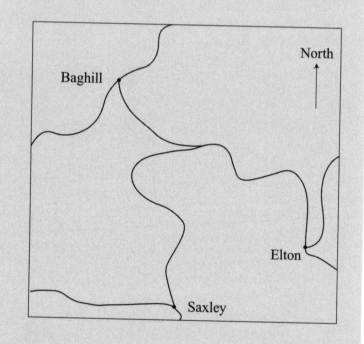

3 2 hikers walk 5 km due south and then 7 km on a bearing of 050°.
   a Use a scale of 1 cm for every 1 km to show their journey.
   b Find the distance of the hikers from their starting point.

4 A submarine travels 40 km due north and then 65 km on a bearing of 300°.
   a Use a scale of 1 cm for every 10 km to show the submarine's journey.
   b Find the distance of the submarine from its starting point.

TASK 20.4

M

You will need a calculator. Give your answers correct to 2 decimal places where necessary. The units are cm.

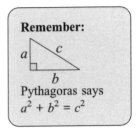

Remember:

$a^2 + b^2 = c^2$

Pythagoras says
$a^2 + b^2 = c^2$

1 Copy the statements below and fill the empty boxes.

a $x^2 = \boxed{}^2 + \boxed{}^2$
$x^2 = 25 + \boxed{}$
$x^2 = \boxed{}$
$x = \sqrt{\boxed{}}$
$x = \boxed{}$

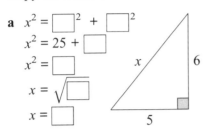

b $x^2 + \boxed{}^2 = 13^2$
$x^2 + \boxed{} = 169$
$x^2 = 169 - \boxed{}$
$x^2 = \boxed{}$
$x = \sqrt{\boxed{}}$
$x = \boxed{}$

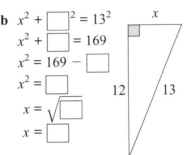

2 Find the length QR.
QR is the hypotenuse.

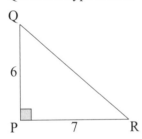

3 Find the length BC.
BC is one of the shorter sides.

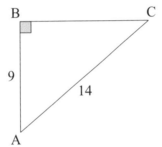

4 Find the length x.
Be careful! Check whether x is the hypotenuse or one of the shorter sides.

a

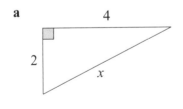

b

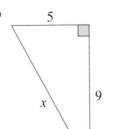

c

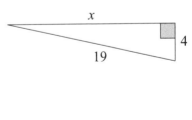

d

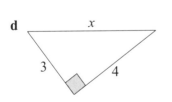

e

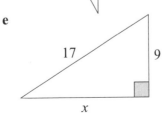

f

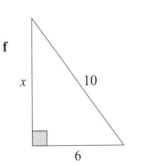

E

1 A ladder of length 8 m reaches 6 m up a vertical wall. How far is the foot of the ladder from the wall?

2 A rectangular TV screen is 21 inches long and 11 inches wide. What is the length of the diagonal of the TV screen?

3 Calculate the perimeter of this triangle.

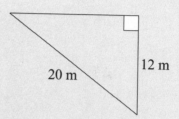

20 m 12 m

4 A plane flies 100 km due south and then a further 150 km due east. How far is the plane from its starting point?

5 A knight on a chessboard moves 2 cm to the right then 4 cm forwards. If the knight moved *directly* from its old position to its new position, how far would it move?

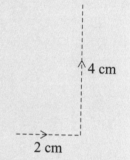

4 cm

2 cm

6 Calculate the area of this triangle.

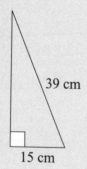

39 cm

15 cm

7 Find *x*.

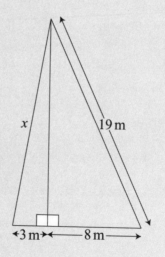

x 19 m

3 m 8 m

8 Find the height of each isosceles triangle below:

a

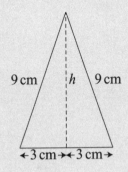

9 cm h 9 cm

←3 cm→←3 cm→

b

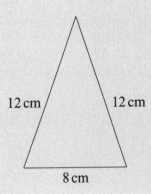

12 cm   12 cm

8 cm

TASK 20.5

M

You may use a calculator.

1 **a** Find the co-ordinates of the midpoint of line PQ.
   b Calculate the length PQ.

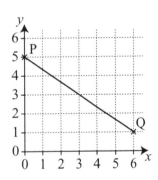

2 **a** Calculate the length of the line joining $(1, 3)$ to $(5, 6)$.
   b Write down the co-ordinates of the midpoint of the line joining $(1, 3)$ to $(5, 6)$.

3 Copy the grid.
   Plot each set of co-ordinates below
   in the order given to form two sides
   of a rectangle.
   Complete the rectangle and write
   down the co-ordinates of the
   missing vertex (corner).
   a $(2, 4), (2, -1), (4, -1), (\quad , \quad)$
   b $(1, 1), (1, 3), (-4, 3), (\quad , \quad)$
   c $(-1, -1), (-5, -1), (-5, -4), (\quad , \quad)$

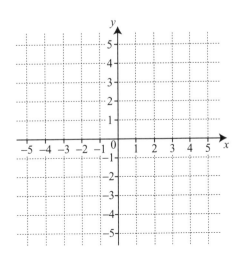

4 **a** Draw an *x*-axis from −2 to 6 and *y*-axis from −3 to 3.
   b ABCD is a parallelogram. A is (1, −2), B is (−1, −2) and C is
       (3, 2). Draw the parallelogram.
   c Write down the co-ordinates of D.
   d Write down the co-ordinates of the midpoint of diagonal AC.
   e Calculate the length of the diagonal AC.

E

1 A has co-ordinates (0, 4, 5).
   Write down the co-ordinates of
   B, C, D, E, F and G.

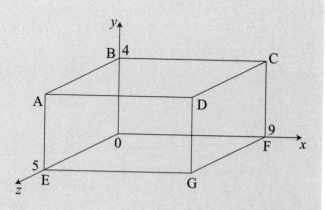

2 Each side of this cube is 2 units long.
   Write down the co-ordinates of the vertices (corners)
   O, P, Q, R, S, T, U and V.

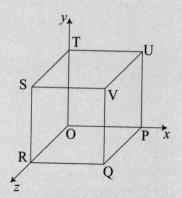

3 OABCD is a square-based pyramid.
   D is directly above the centre of the square base.
   The pyramid has a height of 10 units.
   Write down the co-ordinates of vertex D.

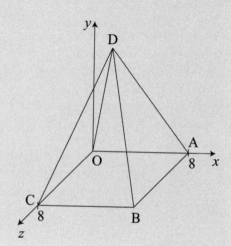

4 **a** Write down the co-ordinates of
     the vertices P, Q, R, S, T, U, V
     and W.
   b Write down the co-ordinates of
     the midpoint of edge VR.
   c Write down the co-ordinates of
     the midpoint of edge PS.
   d Calculate the length PR.

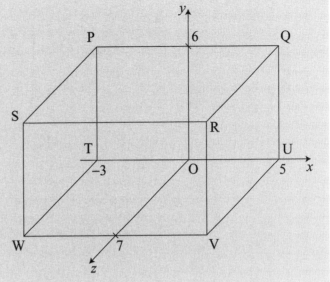